Phonics Review

bju press®

Greenville, South Carolina

NOTE: The fact that materials produced by other publishers may be referred to in this volume does not constitute an endorsement of the content or theological position of materials produced by such publishers. Any references and ancillary materials are listed as an aid to the student or the teacher and in an attempt to maintain the accepted academic standards of the publishing industry.

PHONICS REVIEW

Coordinating Authors
L. Michelle Rosier
Robin E. Scroggins

Authors
Eileen Berry
Dottie Buckley
Addy Forrest
Ann Larson

Contributing Authors
Kristin Alexander
Betty Doeppers
Charlene McCall
Martha Smith
Sarah Smith
Melodye Snyder
Dennae White

Bible Integration
Bryan Smith

Project Editor
Elizabeth Bang Berg

Book Designers
Duane Nichols
Drew Fields

Compositor
Carol Larson

Cover Designer
Ellyson Kalagayan

Cover Illustrator
Julie Speer

Photo Acquisition
DeAnna Landis
Susan Perry
Carla Thomas

Illustration Coordinator
Dave Schuppert

Illustrators
Amber Cheadle
Paula Cheadle
Courtney Godbey
Preston Gravely
Andrea Herbster
Caroline George Lott
Heidi Park
John-Mark Petty
Kathy Pflug
Lynda Slattery
Laura Smith

Project Manager
Benjamin Sinnamon

Photo credits appear on pages 257–58.

© 2007 BJU Press
Greenville, South Carolina 29609

Printed in the United States of America

ISBN 978-1-59166-466-6

15 14 13 12 11 10 9 8 7 6 5

CONGRATULATIONS!

Your search for the very best educational materials available has been completely successful! You have a worktext that is the culmination of decades of research, experience, prayer, and creative energy.

The Facts

Nothing overlooked. Revised and updated. Facts are used as a springboard to stimulate thoughtful questions and guide students to broader applications.

The Foundation

Nothing to conflict with Truth and everything to support it. Truth is the pathway as well as the destination.

The Fun

Nothing boring about this worktext! Student (and teacher) might even forget it's a worktext! Brimming with interesting extras and sparkling with color!

bju **press**.com

Phonics Review is divided into six units with themes of "Going Places." Each unit focuses on a special place to go and a set of phonics skills.

Contents

Unit 1: To Grandma's House   Consonants 1

Unit 2: The Park Is the Place   Short Vowels 41

Unit 3: At the Zoo   Long Vowels.. 69

Unit 4: At the Canyon Rim   Special Vowels 133

Unit 5: Washington, DC   Suffixes and Prefixes.....................................171

Unit 6: Space   Special Sounds and Review 217

Rules and Definitions 249

Index 256

Photo Credits 257

Going Places
Robin E. Scroggins

Going places, special places,
Go all around the town—
To Grandma's house, and to the park,
And to the zoo downtown.

Climb up the trail, explore the woods,
Go anywhere you please—
The Grand Canyon and Washington,
A castle overseas.

Then on a trip *so* far away
To an amazing place—
A trip aboard a rocket ship
Way out in outer space!

So many places to explore
While sitting in your chair.
You wonder how—pick up a book!
Reading takes you there!

Who Should Use Phonics Review?

Phonics Review provides a systematic review of phonics for elementary-age students who have completed some phonics instructions but still struggle with various phonics concepts.

This book may also be used to present an effective foundation in phonics for a student who was introduced to reading with little or no phonics instruction.

In addition, ESL students may benefit from the variety of phonics reinforcement activities in Phonics Review.

The Importance of Language and Reading

For the last several centuries, wherever Christianity has thrived, the work of teaching children to read has also thrived. The first schools in America were started early in the colonial period. Massachusetts Puritans passed the Old Deluder Satan Act in 1647. The law stated that since Satan's purpose was to keep people out of the Scriptures, towns must be required to provide public education to teach people to read the Bible. *The New England Primer*, *The Blue Back Speller*, and several other early reading books used Bible stories or other short stories with morals to teach reading. Other schools in the colonies were also begun, often with religious instruction as the primary goal. God has spoken to the human race primarily through a Book, and those who are devoted to Him should show that devotion by teaching others—especially children—to read.

Enabling children to read the Bible is not the only purpose of reading. Our God is a God of language. He made the world through language (Gen. 1:3ff.), and He is redeeming this world to Himself through language (John 1:1, 18; 6:63; 1 Pet. 1:23). As humans, we are made in God's image (Gen. 1:26–27), and our ability to appreciate and use language plays an important role in our calling to imitate God well.

People who know how to reflect God with their use of language lead fulfilling lives, lives that can be greatly used in God's work of redemption. But acquiring these skills requires years of hard work. It is a long journey, and it begins with one small step—*phonemic awareness*.

What Is Phonics?

Simply stated, phonics is the study of the association of sounds and letters. The spellings of the 44 sounds of the English language, presented in a variety of sequences and levels of intensity, make up the content of all phonics programs. Educators vary in how they believe phonics should be presented. However, the most effective phonics programs are built on the foundational truths relating to the English language.

Patterns in the English Language

The English language, with its 250 ways to spell 44 sounds, presents the student with unusual challenges. The consonant sounds are easily mastered by most children. The vowel sounds, however, need special attention. The consistency in the pronunciation of vowel sounds is tied to the similarities of spelling patterns.

not	noise
no	now
note	noon
north	nook

Examine the list of words at the left. All the words begin with the same two letters, but notice that the vowel *o* represents a variety of sounds. The signal for the sound a vowel represents comes from what follows the vowel in the syllable (not what precedes it.) Therefore, when the student is taught to notice the syllable patterns in the English language, determining vowel sounds is greatly simplified.

Notice the part of each word in the list that is colored red. Each of these patterns can be found in other words as well. These patterns are often referred to as *phonograms*, *word families*, or *rimes* (educational spelling relating to phonograms and word families). For example, the words *dot, got, hot, lot, not, pot, rot, slot, spot, tot,* and *trot* are all in the same word family. Teaching the child to identify the phonograms is a phonics approach that continues to aid the student even as he approaches multisyllable words.

Why Teach Phonics?

A panel examined thirty-eight rigorous studies of early reading instruction. Systematic phonics instruction clearly produced the greatest impact on reading instruction in kindergarten and first grade.[1]

Children who are taught systematic phonics at the onset of their reading instruction enjoy a great advantage. Children who transfer from schools or programs that teach little or no phonics make great gains when they enter a systematic phonics program. A strong phonics program will provide ample practice in identifying and decoding words based upon the syllable patterns.

How Should This Book Be Used?

This book is designed to be used independently by the student. However, the teacher may choose to give as much assistance as is appropriate.

On some pages a picture is given and the student is asked to identify the beginning, middle, or ending sound. Some students, especially in an ESL setting, may not be sure of the vocabulary associated with a certain picture. Since the focus is on the sound, not the identification of the vocabulary, the teacher may choose to read the words given in the Answer Key.

---

1. Katherine Townsend and Herbert J. Walberg, "Teaching Initial Reading: What a Difference the Sounds Make!" *Communiqué* 30, no. 1 (2001): 31–32.

Unit 1

To Grandma's House

Robin E. Scroggins

I love to go to Grandma's house.
It's such a special place.
When I get there I love to see
My grandma's smiling face!

She always has a hug for me—
And usually a snack.
She sometimes plays a game with me
Or else I play out back.

I really like to climb the trees
In my grandma's backyard.
My sister likes the dress-up trunk;
She says the tree's too hard!

My grandma likes to have me help
When she's at the computer.
Can you believe, when she was young,
They didn't have computers!

She has some neat things at her house.
The one called *typewriter*
Is like a strange computer, but
It has no monitor!

She has a radio she plays
But not a CD player.
She has a funny spinning thing
She calls a "record player."

My grandma loves to knit and bake.
She reads great books with me.
Besides all this—my grandpa's there!
It's the best place to be!

I love to go to Grandma's house;
I know she loves me too!
But most importantly, I think,
She says, "I pray for you."

Unit 1 Contents

Initial Consonant Sounds 3–4
Final Consonant Sounds 5–6
Initial and Final Consonant Sounds 7–8
Medial Consonant Sounds 9–10
Double Consonants 11
Digraph *ck* 12
L Blends 13–14
R Blends 15–16
S Blends 17
S Blends; Initial Three-Letter Blends 18
Initial Blends 19–21
Initial Three-Letter Blends 22
Review 23–24
Final Blends 25–28
Blends 29–30
Initial Digraphs *ch, sh* 31
Initial Digraphs *th, wh* 32
Final Digraphs *ch, sh, th* 33
Digraphs 34–36
Blends and Digraphs 37–38
Checkup 39–40

Mark the consonant you hear at the beginning of each word.

Name _____

1. ○ n   ○ h

2. ○ t   ○ f

3. ○ y   ○ w

4. ○ g   ○ f

5. ○ g   ○ b

6. ○ r   ○ s

7. ○ m   ○ p

8. ○ j   ○ k

9. ○ d   ○ l

10. ○ z   ○ s

11. ○ v   ○ n

12. ○ l   ○ y

Phonics Review
Skill: initial consonant sounds

Write the missing letter.

1. _____onkey

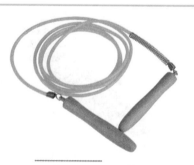

2. _____lower

3. _____iger

4. _____ails

5. _____orse

6. _____ump rope

7. _____and

8. _____ift

9. _____at

10. _____eer

11. _____emon

12. _____uilt

Phonics Review
Skill: initial consonant sounds

Mark the letter for the ending sound.

1. ○ s   ○ b

2. ○ q   ○ l

3. ○ d   ○ v

4. ○ h   ○ t

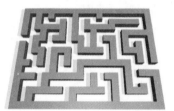

5. ○ j   ○ z

6. ○ x   ○ m

7. ○ c   ○ p

8. ○ k   ○ w

9. ○ g   ○ r

10. ○ f   ○ n

Phonics Review
Skill: final consonant sounds

Write the letter for the ending sound.

1. bo_____

2. gu_____

3. brea_____

4. ba_____

5. goa_____

6. bow_____

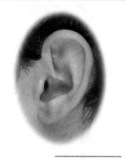

7. ea_____

8. ca_____

9. gumdro_____

10. tu_____

11. hor_____

12. lea_____

Phonics Review
Skill: final consonant sounds

Write the beginning and ending letters.

1. _____ o _____

2. _____ a _____

3. _____ o _____

4. _____ oa _____

5. _____ a _____

6. _____ a _____

7. _____ a _____

8. _____ ar _____

9. _____ uee _____

10. _____ i _____

11. _____ u _____

12. _____ o _____

Phonics Review
Skill: initial and final consonant sounds

Write the beginning and ending letters.

 1. ____o____

 2. ____a____

 3. ____i____

 4. ____a____

 5. ____e____

 6. ____e____

 7. ____oo____

 8. ____a____

 9. ____i____

 10. ____oo____

 11. ____a____

 12. ____ai____

8

Mark the consonant for the sound you hear in the middle.

Name _____

1.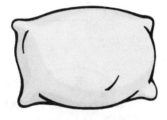
   ○ t
   ○ q

2.
   ○ m
   ○ s

3.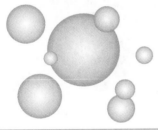
   ○ d
   ○ l

4.
   ○ r
   ○ n

5.
   ○ g
   ○ m

6.
   ○ z
   ○ f

7.
   ○ b
   ○ q

8.
   ○ r
   ○ s

9.
   ○ n
   ○ d

10.
   ○ b
   ○ z

11.
   ○ v
   ○ x

12.
   ○ k
   ○ t

Phonics Review
Skill: medial consonant sounds

Write the consonant for the sound in the middle.

1. _____

2. _____

3. _____

4. _____

5. _____

6. _____

7. _____

8. _____

9. _____

10. _____

11. _____

12. _____

Phonics Review
Skill: medial consonant sounds

When one consonant sound is heard, the sound may be spelled with two consonants.
Examples: cu**ff**, mi**ss**, bu**zz**, bu**tt**er

Name _____

Write the two consonants to complete each word.

1. e_____

2. cro_____

3. hi_____

4. be_____

5. a_____

6. cli_____

Write the two consonants that make the middle sound.

7. ca_____ots

8. ha_____er

9. bu_____on

Write *ck* to complete each word.

1. lo_____

2. ta_____

3. bla_____

4. bri_____

5. blo_____

6. sti_____

Write the two consonants that make the /k/ sound.

7. sti_____er

8. wre_____er

9. chi_____en

10. ro_____et

12

A consonant blend is formed when two consonant sounds are blended together at the beginning of a word.
Examples: **clock**, **sled**

Name _____

Mark the consonant blend at the beginning of each word.

1. ○ gl   ○ pl

2. ○ bl   ○ cl

3. ○ gl   ○ sl

4. ○ bl   ○ cl

5. ○ gl   ○ bl

6. ○ fl   ○ bl

7. ○ fl   ○ pl

8. ○ cl   ○ bl

9. ○ gl   ○ bl

10. ○ sl   ○ pl

11. ○ fl   ○ pl

12. ○ pl   ○ gl

Phonics Review
Skill: *l* blends

13

Write the consonant blend.

1. _____ams

2. _____ub

3. _____ast

4. _____ock

5. _____ender

6. _____ayground

7. _____ock

8. _____ay

9. _____ed

14

A consonant blend is formed when two consonant sounds are blended together at the beginning of a word.
Examples: **tr**ick, **dr**op

Name _____

Write *br* or *pr* to complete each word.

1. _____ead

2. _____idge

3. _____etzel

4. _____ize

Write *tr* or *fr* to complete each word.

5. _____umpet

6. _____own

7. _____ash

8. _____iangle

Write *cr*, *gr*, or *dr* to complete each word.

9. _____adle

10. _____ips

11. _____ayon

12. _____een

Phonics Review
Skill: *r* blends

15

Write the consonant blend to complete each word.

1. _____ain

2. _____og

3. _____apes

4. _____ess

5. _____ay

6. _____ass

7. _____um

8. _____ide

9. _____oss

10. _____own

11. _____ee

12. _____uck

Phonics Review
Skill: *r* blends

A consonant blend is formed when two consonant sounds are blended together at the beginning of a word.
Examples: **sk**ip, **sc**are

Write *sc* or *sl* to complete each word.

1. _____ale

2. _____ippers

3. _____ed

4. _____arf

Write *sq*, *sn*, or *sm* to complete each word.

5. _____owman

6. _____ail

7. _____ile

8. _____uirrel

Write *st* or *sk* to complete each word.

9. _____airs

10. _____y

11. _____ool

12. _____ates

A consonant blend is formed when two or three consonant sounds are blended together at the beginning of a word.
Examples: **scrape**, **splinter**, **spring**, **strong**

Mark the consonant blend at the beginning of each word.

1. ○ sn   ○ sm

2. ○ st   ○ sk

3. ○ sm   ○ sq

4. ○ st   ○ sl

5. ○ spl   ○ st

6. ○ sw   ○ str

7. ○ st   ○ sc

8. ○ sl   ○ scr

9. ○ spr   ○ sl

10. ○ sw   ○ str

11. ○ str   ○ scr

12. ○ sm   ○ spr

18

Phonics Review
Skills: *s* blends; initial three-letter blends

Write the blend to complete each word.

1. _____uash

2. _____imp

3. _____ill

4. _____ib

5. _____ick

6. _____us

7. _____ar

8. _____ipes

9. _____iff

10. _____ay

Mark the correct word.

1. ◯ stem   ◯ skim

2. ◯ frog   ◯ flag

3. ◯ slap   ◯ snap

4. ◯ trap   ◯ trip

5. ◯ spill   ◯ still

6. ◯ drill   ◯ grill

7. ◯ clot   ◯ crop

8. ◯ straps   ◯ scraps

9. ◯ plus   ◯ plug

10. ◯ glass   ◯ grass

Write the blend to complete each word.

1. _____ower

2. _____anket

3. _____um

4. _____uash

5. _____um

6. _____own

7. _____ass

8. _____ams

9. _____ake

10. _____one

11. _____ide

12. _____ates

Phonics Review
Skill: initial blends

Write *scr*, *spl*, or *str* to complete each word.

1. _____ambled eggs

2. _____it

3. _____atter

4. _____aw

5. _____apbook

6. _____oller

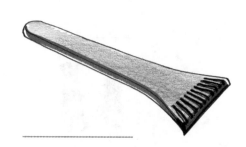

7. _____aper

8. _____eamers

Phonics Review
Skill: initial three-letter blends

Write *k* or *ck* to complete each word.

1. _____itchen

2. so_____

3. ro_____

4. _____ite

5. _____angaroo

6. sti_____

Mark the consonant for the sound you hear in the middle.

7. ○ v   ○ x

8. ○ n   ○ s

9. ○ t   ○ l

10. ○ q   ○ f

Phonics Review: *Review*
Skills: *k, ck*; medial consonant sounds

Mark the correct word.

1. ○ mess ○ dress

2. ○ nail ○ snail

3. ○ class ○ glass

4. ○ spoon ○ soon

Write the blend to complete each word.

5. _____etzel

6. _____ead

7. _____ust

8. _____ain

Draw a line from the word to the correct picture.

9. scrub

10. spring

11. stroller

24

Phonics Review: *Review*
Skill: initial blends

A consonant blend is formed when two consonant sounds are blended together at the end of a word.
Examples: dri**nk**, si**lk**, ju**mp**, swi**ft**

Name _____

Write the ending blend to complete each word.

1. sku_____

2. cra_____

3. tru_____

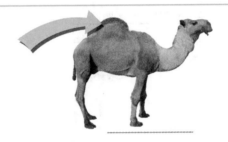

4. hu_____

5. bu_____

6. ra_____

7. mi_____

8. le_____

Phonics Review
Skill: final blends

25

Write the ending blend to complete each word.

1. ra_____

2. bu_____

3. sta_____

4. gi_____

5. de_____

6. be_____

7. e_____

8. a_____

9. dri_____

10. shie_____

Phonics Review
Skill: final blends

_____
Name

Mark the correct word.

1. ◯ nest ◯ next

2. ◯ mask ◯ mast

3. ◯ band ◯ bank

4. ◯ last ◯ lamp

5. ◯ spent ◯ swept

6. ◯ past ◯ pink

7. ◯ golf ◯ gust

8. ◯ text ◯ tent

9. ◯ send ◯ sink

10. ◯ test ◯ tend

Mark the correct word.

1. ◯ mist   ◯ mint

2. ◯ fat   ◯ fact

3. ◯ quilt   ◯ quit

4. ◯ gulp   ◯ gull

5. ◯ list   ◯ link

6. ◯ camp   ◯ cart

7. ◯ post   ◯ pond

8. ◯ text   ◯ tend

9. ◯ melt   ◯ mast

10. ◯ grass   ◯ grasp

Phonics Review
Skill: final blends

Mark the correct word.

Name

1. ○ raft ○ rest

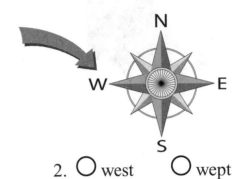

2. ○ west ○ wept

3. ○ slept ○ crept

4. ○ next ○ nest

5. ○ squint ○ splint

6. ○ steps ○ skips

7. ○ flag ○ frog

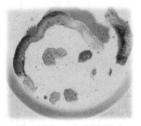

8. ○ trusts ○ crusts

9. ○ mint ○ mend

10. ○ straps ○ scraps

Phonics Review
Skill: blends

Write the missing consonant blends.

1. tu_____

2. _____ender

3. sto_____

4. le_____

5. hu_____

6. _____ess

7. _____incess

8. _____and

9. _____opper

10. _____ain

Phonics Review
Skill: blends

A consonant digraph is formed when two consonants together make one sound.
Examples: **shot**, **chin**, **thank**, **whip**

Name _____

Mark the consonant digraph *ch* or *sh* at the beginning of each word.

1. ◯ ch   ◯ sh

2. ◯ ch   ◯ sh

3. ◯ ch   ◯ sh

4. ◯ ch   ◯ sh

5. ◯ ch   ◯ sh

6. ◯ ch   ◯ sh

Write *ch* or *sh* to complete each word.

7. _____eep

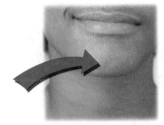 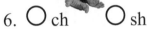

8. _____in

9. _____ips

10. _____eck

11. _____elf

12. _____ed

Phonics Review
Skill: initial digraphs *ch*, *sh*

31

Mark the consonant digraph *th* or *wh* at the beginning of each word.

1. ◯ th ◯ wh

2. ◯ th ◯ wh

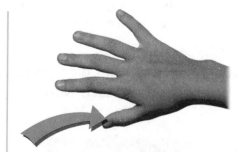

3. ◯ th ◯ wh

4. ◯ th ◯ wh

5. ◯ th ◯ wh

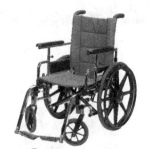

6. ◯ th ◯ wh

Write *th* or *wh* to complete each word.

7. _____iskers

8. _____irty

9. _____eel

10. _____rone

11. _____en

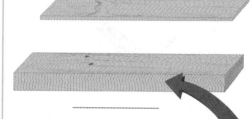

12. _____ick

Phonics Review
Skill: initial digraphs *th*, *wh*

Mark the consonant digraph at the end of each word.

1. ○ ch ○ sh ○ th

2. ○ ch ○ sh ○ th

3. ○ ch ○ sh ○ th

4. ○ ch ○ sh ○ th

5. ○ ch ○ sh ○ th

6. ○ ch ○ sh ○ th

7. ○ ch ○ sh ○ th

8. ○ ch ○ sh ○ th

Phonics Review
Skill: final digraphs *ch*, *sh*, *th*

Mark the correct word.

1. O moth   O mash

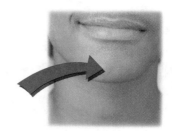

2. O chin   O shin

3. O cash   O cast

4. O flat   O flash

5. O slip   O ship

6. O chop   O shop

7. O flips   O chips

8. O crank   O crash

Phonics Review
Skill: digraphs

Mark the consonant digraph at the beginning of each word.

1. ○ ch   ○ sh   ○ wh

2. ○ ch   ○ th   ○ wh

3. ○ sh   ○ th   ○ wh

4. ○ ch   ○ th   ○ wh

5. ○ ch   ○ sh   ○ th

6. ○ ch   ○ sh   ○ wh

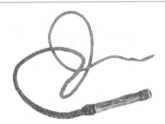

7. ○ ch   ○ sh   ○ wh

8. ○ ch   ○ sh   ○ th

9. ○ ch   ○ th   ○ wh

10. ○ sh   ○ th   ○ wh

Phonics Review
Skill: digraphs

Write the consonant digraph at the end of each word.

1. spla_____

2. pa_____

3. wrea_____

4. lun_____

5. bran_____

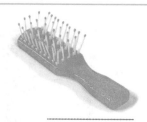

6. bru_____

7. tra_____

8. fi_____

9. ba_____

10. ben_____

Phonics Review
Skill: digraphs

Mark the beginning blend or digraph in each word.   Name _____

1. ◯ tr   ◯ th

2. ◯ fr   ◯ cl

3. ◯ pr   ◯ tr

4. ◯ sp   ◯ sq

5. ◯ cr   ◯ ch

6. ◯ ch   ◯ sh

Mark the ending blend or digraph in each word.

7. ◯ ch   ◯ sh

8. ◯ lp   ◯ mp

9. ◯ ch   ◯ sh

10. ◯ nd   ◯ nk

11. ◯ th   ◯ ch

12. ◯ nk   ◯ mp

Phonics Review
Skill: blends and digraphs

Write the missing letters.

1. di_____

2. _____in

3. bru_____

4. _____ant

5. _____ocks

6. sku_____

7. tee_____

8. si_____

9. _____ug

38

Write the two consonants that make the middle sound.

Name _____

1. bu_____er

2. mu_____in

3. ne_____lace

4. ba_____pack

Write the blend to complete each word.

5. sta_____

6. _____ide

7. _____uck

8. ba_____

9. tru_____

10. _____ool

Mark the letters for the beginning sound.

11.

○ spl
○ str

12.

○ spr
○ scr

Write the letters to complete each word.

1. _____ell

2. bran_____

3. _____istle

4. por_____

5. _____eep

6. _____air

7. _____erry

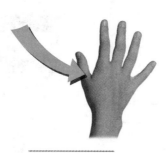

8. _____umb

9. mu_____rooms

10. _____orn

11. mo_____er

12. _____alk

Phonics Review: Checkup
Skill: digraphs

Unit 2

The Park Is the Place

Eileen M. Berry

When you want to look ants in the eye,
Or sail up in a swing to the sky,
Or have a new kite to fly,
The park is the place to be.

You can zoom quick-as-light down the slide,
Or bump seesaws from side to side.
There are hundreds of places to hide!
The park is the place to be.

You can run with your face to the breeze,
Climb the jungle-gym bars if you please,
Or hang upside down by your knees!
The park is the place to be.

The park is the place to be, to be,
The park is the place for me!

Unit 2 Contents

Short *a* 43–44

Short *e* 45–46

Short *i* 47–48

Short *o* 49–50

Short *u* 51–52

Review 53–54

Rhyming Words 55–56

Short Vowels and -*le* 57–59

Spelling Short-Vowel Words 60–62

Composition 63

Short Vowels 64

Reading a Story 65–66

Checkup 67–68

A vowel may say more than one sound. When a word or syllable has one vowel followed by one or more consonants, the vowel usually says its short sound. Examples: Short *a* says /ă/ as in *bag* and *tack*.

Name _____

Circle the pictures that have the short *a* sound.

1.

2.

3.

4.

5.

6.

7.

8.

9.

10.

11.

12.

Phonics Review
Skill: /ă/

Draw a line from the word to the correct picture.

1. trash

2. glass

3. jacks

4. pants

5. cats

6. plant

7. raft

8. rack

9. tank

10. cans

Phonics Review
Skill: /ă/

When a word or syllable has one vowel followed by one or more consonants, the vowel usually says its short sound.

Examples: Short *e* says /ĕ/ as in *pet* and *rest*.

Circle the pictures that have the short *e* sound.

1.

2.

3.

4.

5.

6.

7.

8.

9.

10.

11.

12.

Write the correct word under each picture.

chest   deck   elk   steps

1. _____

2. _____

3. _____

4. _____

dent   desk   left   pen

5. _____

6. _____

7. _____

8. _____

belt   check   men   shelf

9. _____

10. _____

11. _____

12. _____

46

Phonics Review
Skill: /ĕ/

When a word or syllable has one vowel followed by one or more consonants, the vowel usually says its short sound.

Examples: Short *i* says /ĭ/ as in *dip* and *fish*.

Name _____

Draw a line from the word to the correct picture.

1. milk

2. whip

3. twins

4. grill

5. limp

6. zip

7. pills

8. grin

9. cliff

10. quilt

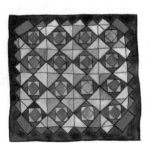

Phonics Review
Skill: /ĭ/

47

Write the correct word under each picture.

chimp   crib   mix   ring

1. _____

2. _____

3. _____

4. _____

chick   drip   kick   pink

5. _____

6. _____

7. _____

8. _____

spill   string   swing   whisk

9. _____

10. _____

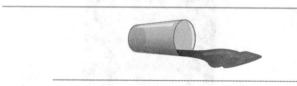

11. _____

12. _____

48

When a word or syllable has one vowel followed by one or more consonants, the vowel usually says its short sound.
Examples: Short *o* says /ŏ/ in *mom* and *rock*.

Draw a line from the word to the correct picture.

1. ox

2. cob

3. pot

4. sock

5. robin

6. hot dog

7. dots

8. clock

9. rocks

10. dock

Phonics Review
Skill: /ŏ/

49

Write the correct word under each picture.

blocks   box   rock   shot

1. _____

2. _____

3. _____

4. _____

cot   mop   shop   spots

5. _____

6. _____

7. _____

8. _____

drops   mom   pond   slot

9. _____

10. _____

11. _____

12. _____

50

Name _____

Draw a line from the word to the correct picture.

1. bun

2. brush

3. drum

4. gull

5. bunks

---

6. lunch

7. plus

8. clubs

9. strum

10. bulb

$26 + 31$

Write the correct word under each picture.

gum mud nuts stump

1. _____

2. _____

3. _____

4. _____

duck plug plum pup

5. _____

6. _____

7. _____

8. _____

bug bus hump mug

9. _____

10. _____

11. _____

12. _____

52

Mark the vowel sound you hear in the middle of each word.

1. ○ a   ○ e   ○ i   ○ o   ○ u

2. ○ a   ○ e   ○ i   ○ o   ○ u

3. ○ a   ○ e   ○ i   ○ o   ○ u

4. ○ a   ○ e   ○ i   ○ o   ○ u

5. ○ a   ○ e   ○ i   ○ o   ○ u

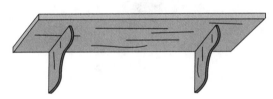

6. ○ a   ○ e   ○ i   ○ o   ○ u

7. ○ a   ○ e   ○ i   ○ o   ○ u

8. ○ a   ○ e   ○ i   ○ o   ○ u

9. ○ a   ○ e   ○ i   ○ o   ○ u

10. ○ a   ○ e   ○ i   ○ o   ○ u

Phonics Review: *Review*
Skill: short-vowel sounds

Write a short-vowel word to name each picture.

1. ____ ____ ____ ____

2. ____ ____ ____ ____

3. ____ ____ ____ ____ ____

4. ____ ____ ____ ____

5. ____ ____ ____ ____ ____

6. ____ ____ ____ ____

7. ____ ____ ____

8. ____ ____ ____ ____

9. ____ ____ ____

10. ____ ____ ____ ____

54

Mark the word that rhymes with each picture.

1.
   - ○ patch
   - ○ shift
   - ○ crust

2.
   - ○ bell
   - ○ melt
   - ○ milk

3.
   - ○ pan
   - ○ fun
   - ○ then

4.
   - ○ skip
   - ○ bunk
   - ○ rat

5.
   - ○ plan
   - ○ flap
   - ○ ham

6.
   - ○ pants
   - ○ add
   - ○ pens

7.
   - ○ crab
   - ○ cast
   - ○ trust

8.
   - ○ crop
   - ○ strap
   - ○ stomp

9.
   - ○ lots
   - ○ spin
   - ○ socks

10.
    - ○ shell
    - ○ clap
    - ○ trip

Phonics Review
Skill: rhyming words

Mark the word that does **not** rhyme.

1. ○ ring   ○ sing   ○ hang   ○ string

2. ○ must   ○ pest   ○ just   ○ crust

3. ○ sack   ○ black   ○ sick   ○ stack

4. ○ small   ○ shell   ○ smell   ○ spell

5. ○ shot   ○ flat   ○ plot   ○ spot

6. ○ hand   ○ send   ○ land   ○ sand

7. ○ fled   ○ shed   ○ trod   ○ bled

8. ○ bent   ○ dent   ○ pant   ○ spent

9. ○ clip   ○ strip   ○ slip   ○ slop

10. ○ mend   ○ stand   ○ lend   ○ blend

Draw lines to match the rhyming words.

11. bath   shift

12. bench   math

13. swift   stump

14. shock   wrench

15. thump   stock

56

Phonics Review
Skill: rhyming words

When a vowel is followed by two consonants and -*le*, it has a short vowel sound. The -*le* at the end of a word says /əl/.

Examples: gig**gle**, crac**kle**, twink**le**

Write the vowel in each word.

1. c _____ ttle

2. b _____ ttle

3. f _____ ddle

4. sp _____ ckle

5. c _____ ddle

6. r _____ ttle

Write the two missing consonants in each word.

7. bu _____ les

8. ha _____ le

9. a _____ le

10. pi _____ le

Write the correct word under each picture.

bundle	candle	griddle

1. _____

2. _____

3. _____

paddle	puzzle	ruffle

4. _____

5. _____

6. _____

buckle	puddle	thimble

7. _____

8. _____

9. _____

Phonics Review
Skill: short vowels and -le

Write the correct word under each picture.

Name _____

jingle   kettle   middle

1. _____

2. _____

3. _____

ankle   jungle   wrinkle

4. _____

5. _____

6. _____

scribbles   sprinkles   wobbles

7. _____

8. _____

9. _____

Phonics Review
Skill: short vowels and -le

Write a short-vowel word to name each picture.

1. _____ _____ _____

2. _____ _____ _____

3. _____ _____ _____

4. _____ _____ _____

5. _____ _____ _____

6. _____ _____ _____

7. _____ _____ _____

8. _____ _____ _____ _____

9. _____ _____ _____

10. _____ _____ _____

11. _____ _____ _____

12. _____ _____ _____

Phonics Review
Skill: spelling short-vowel words

Write two new words by changing the vowel.

1. cut   *cat*   *cot*

2. bad

3. beg

4. fan

5. ham

6. hut

7. track

8. pack

9. pit

10. sit

Phonics Review
Skill: spelling short-vowel words

Write two more words in the same word family.

1. fish

__dish__

__wish__

2. shell

3. clock

4. king

5. ship

6. bug

7. sink

8. van

9. hat

10. bend

11. crop

12. dust

62

Phonics Review
Skill: spelling short-vowel words

Imagine a trip to your favorite park.
Who would you go with?
What would you do?

Name

Use the words in the box or your own words to write about the park.

trip	spin	swim	thrill
run	swing	dig	pebbles
tag	bug	stick	tumble
jump	grass	rest	flip

Phonics Review
Skill: composition

Complete the crossword puzzle
using the words in the box.

| ducks | hill | jump | little | pickle |
| pond | puddle | stick | swing | tag |

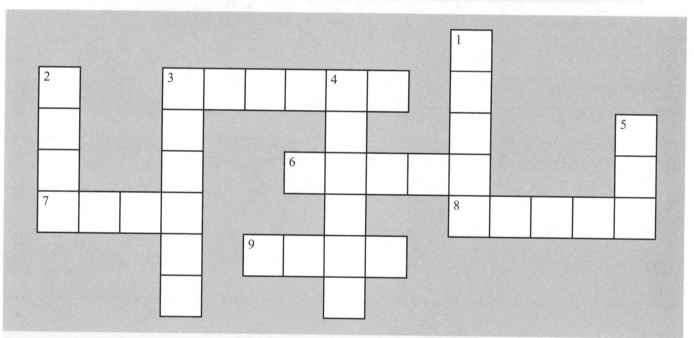

Across

3. something in a picnic lunch
6. toss this for a dog
7. where ducks and frogs live
8. what you do with a bat
9. what Jack and Jill went up

Down

1. these swim in a pond
2. a big hop
3. a wet or muddy spot
4. not big
5. run and tap someone

Phonics Review
Skill: short vowels

4

Max helps himself to the bag of chips! Then he flops on the grass for a nap. Liz and Kent giggle. "That Max!"

Name _____

That Max!

Mom, Dad, Kent, and Liz set off for the park. Kent and Liz jog the last block. Their black dog, Max, trots with them.

FLAV'S POTATO CHIPS

Mom sits on the quilt. They unpack the lunch. Max runs to the quilt. "Toss him a chip, Dad." Max has a chip.

Liz pets Max. She sits in a swing. Max licks her hand. Kent gets in the sandbox. Max jumps in too. He rolls and wiggles in the sand. Liz giggles. "That Max is funny."

Write the vowel in each word.

1. b_____nch

2. bl_____ck

3. br_____ck

Write a short-vowel word to name each picture.

4. ____ ____ ____ ____

5. ____ ____ ____ ____

6. ____ ____ ____

Mark the correct word.

7. ◯ chips ◯ chops

8. ◯ tent ◯ tint

9. ◯ duck ◯ deck

10. ◯ luck ◯ lock

11. ◯ flog ◯ flag

12. ◯ truck ◯ track

Phonics Review: *Checkup*
Skill: short vowels

Draw a line from the word to the correct picture.

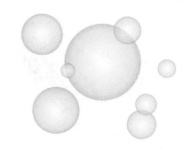

1. puzzle

2. apple

3. tangle

4. bubbles

Draw a line from the word to the picture of a **rhyming** word.

5. tracks

6. thick

7. swish

8. handle

Write a rhyming word.

9. spin

_____

10. thick

_____

11. grand

_____

12. damp

_____

Phonics Review: Checkup
Skills: words with *-le*; rhyming words

Unit 3

At the Zoo

Robin E. Scroggins

When John Mark and Jonathan went to the zoo,
A breeze was blowing, but the sky was quite blue.
They saw many animals: bears and wild dogs,
Flamingos and rhinos and little striped frogs.

John Mark was excited and started to run.
His cap blew away, and the chase had begun.
It landed on top of the tallest giraffe,
And Fred the chimpanzee looked like he would laugh.

It fell in the water right over a seal,
Who popped up to wear it while he ate his meal.
He leaped for a fish—then the cap tumbled clear.
As Jonathan caught it, the crowd gave a cheer.

John Mark was all smiles as he checked his map.
They'd seen all the animals; he had his cap.
The boys thought, "The zoo's not the best place to roam."
So John Mark and Jonathan said, "Let's go home!"

Unit 3 Contents

Long *a* 71

Long *a* VCe 72

Long *a* Digraph *ai* 73

Long *a* Digraph *ay* 74

Long *a* 75

Long and Short *a*; Breve and Macron 76

Long *e* 77

Long *e* Digraphs *ea, ee* 78

Long *e* Open Syllables 79

Long *e* 80–81

Long and Short *e*; Breve and Macron 82

Long and Short *a* and *e* 83

Long *a* and *e* 84

Long *i* 85

Long *i* VCe 86

Long *i* as *igh* 87

Long and Short *i* 88

Long *i* 89

Long and Short *a, e, i* 90

Long *o* 91

Long *o* VCe 92

Long *o* Digraphs *oa, ow* 93

Long Vowels in Open Syllables 94

Long *o* 95

Long and Short *o*; Breve and Macron 96

Long-Vowel Rhymes 97

Long and Short Vowels 98

Long *u* 99–100

Long and Short *u* 101

Long-Vowel Review 102

Review 103–4

-*le* after Long Vowels 105

-*le* after Long and Short Vowels; Breve and Macron . . . 106

y as Long *i* 107–8

y as Long *e* 109–10

y as Long *i* and Long *e* 111–12

Long Vowels in Closed Syllables 113–14

Hard and Soft *c* 115–16

Hard and Soft *g* 117–18

Hard and Soft *c* and *g* 119

Soft *c* and *g* 120

Long *e* Spelled *ie* 121

Long *e* and *i* 122

Compound Words 123–24

Spelling Long-Vowel Words 125

Long-Vowel Words 126

Composition 127

Reading Long-Vowel Words 128

Reading a Story 129–30

Checkup 131–32

The vowel letter *a* sometimes says its long sound.
Examples: rake, rain

Circle the pictures that have the long *a* sound.

1.

2.

3.

4.

5.

6.

7.

8.

9.

10.

11.

12.

Phonics Review
Skill: /ā/

Mark the correct word.

1. ◯ bale   ◯ ball

2. ◯ take   ◯ tack

3. ◯ mat   ◯ mate

4. ◯ cap   ◯ cape

5. ◯ pane   ◯ pan

6. ◯ rack   ◯ rake

7. ◯ whale   ◯ wall

8. ◯ rate   ◯ rat

9. ◯ man   ◯ mane

10. ◯ tape   ◯ tap

Phonics Review
Skill: /ā/ in VCe pattern

When two vowels are together, often the first vowel is long and the second one is silent.
Examples: trail, brain

braid	chain	mail	nail
pail	paint	rain	snail
tail	train		

Write the correct word under each picture.

1. _____

2. _____

3. _____

4. _____

5. _____

6. _____

7. _____

8. _____

9. _____

10. _____

Phonics Review
Skill: vowel digraph *ai* as /ā/

Write an *ay* word to name each picture.

clay	day	gray	hay	jay
May	play	pray	ray	tray

1. _____

2. _____

3. _____

4. _____

5. _____

6. _____

7. _____

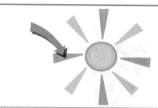

8. _____

9. _____

10. _____

Phonics Review
Skill: vowel digraph *ay* as /ā/

Write the word to complete each sentence.

| pain | play | rain | stay | today |

_____

1. Dave wants to _____.

_____

2. Dave plays in the _____.

_____

3. Dave fell on his ankle _____.

_____

4. He is in _____.

_____

5. He must _____ and rest.

| ate | bake | cake | gave | tray |

_____

6. I made a _____.

_____

7. Mom helped me _____ it.

_____

8. My cake was on a _____.

_____

9. I _____ my cake to Dad.

_____

10. Dad _____ my cake.

Phonics Review
Skill: /ā/

Mark each long *a* with a – or ˘.
Mark each short *a* with a – or ˘.

1. can	2. cane
3. plain	4. plan

A *macron* – may be written over a vowel to show that it makes its long sound.
Example: bāit

A *breve* ˘ may be written over a vowel to show that it makes its short sound.
Example: băt

Write each word in the correct column.

back	bake	cap	cape	mat
mate	paints	pants	shack	shake

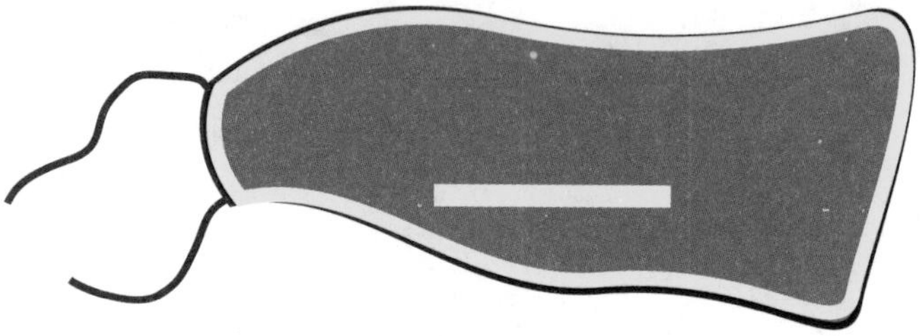

Long *a*

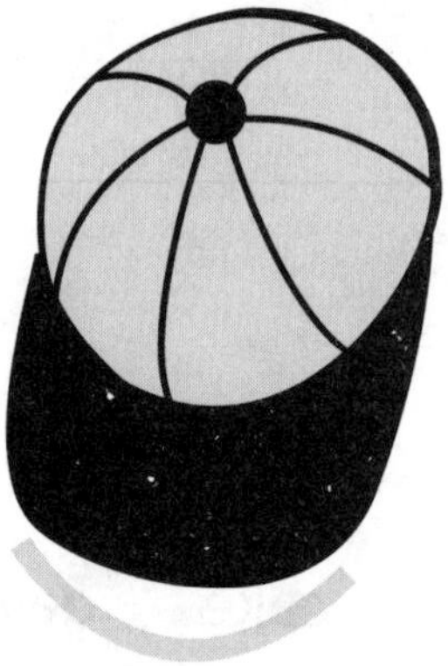

Short *a*

The vowel letter *e* sometimes says its long sound.
Examples: bean, bees

Name _____

Circle the pictures that have the long *e* sound.

1.

2.

3.

4.

5.

6.

7.

8.

9.

10.

11.

12.

Phonics Review
Skill: /ē/

Write the correct word under each picture.

beach	beans	feet	leaf
leash	peach	peacock	peel
queen	seagull	seashell	tea

1. _____

2. _____

3. _____

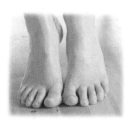

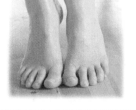

4. _____

5. _____

6. _____

7. _____

8. _____

9. _____

10. _____

11. _____

12. _____

Phonics Review
Skill: vowel digraphs *ea, ee* as /ē/

> When a vowel is alone at the end of a word or syllable, it often says its long sound.
> Example: we

Name _____

Write the word to complete each sentence.

| be | he | me | she | we |

1. _____ is my uncle.

2. My uncle gave _____ a hat like his.

3. My sister says _____ needs one too.

4. Her hat will have to _____ little.

5. Then _____ will each have a hat.

| feed | Pete | seals | see | sleep |

6. _____ the zookeeper met us at the gate.

7. He took us to _____ the sloths.

8. They _____ in the trees.

9. Next we got to see the _____ .

10. Pete let us _____ them.

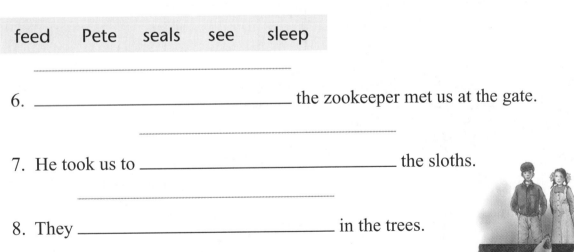

Phonics Review
Skill: /ē/ in open syllables

79

Complete the crossword puzzle using the words in the box.

donkey	feed	feet	keep
leaf	meat	neat	peel
seal	sheep	squeak	tree

Across

2. animal that has a fleece
3. grows from a stem
5. animal that has long ears
7. a kind of plant
8. take care of
10. food for wild beasts
11. give an animal something to eat

Down

1. animal that eats fish
2. a tiny sound
4. pigs have four of these
6. clean
9. skin of a banana

Phonics Review
Skill: /ē/

Circle the correct word.

1. **We / Me** went on a trip to the shore.

2. We stayed in a nice **treat / beach** house near the water.

3. Dad had to fix the **lake / leak** in the boat.

4. Dad took the boat out to the **reef / beef** .

5. He **peeled / reeled** in lots of fish.

6. Mom made a **meal / mean** with Dad's catch.

7. **Steam / Street** came from yummy fish chowder.

8. I picked up **seashore / seashells** along the shore.

9. Soon it was time to **leaf / leave** .

10. We had a great **week / peek** together.

Phonics Review
Skill: /ē/

81

Put a macron or breve over the first vowel in each word.
Use a − to mark a long *e*. Use a �‿ to mark a short *e*.
Use a green crayon to color the balloons with long *e* words.
Use a red crayon to color the balloons with short *e* words.

h̄eel

lĕft

1. sheet

2. leap

3. meat

4. keep

5. need

6. dent

7. blend

8. feet

9. rest

10. bee

11. sleeve

12. check

Phonics Review
Skills: /ē/, /ĕ/; breve and macron

Mark the correct word.

1. ○ pan   ○ pane

2. ○ beds   ○ beads

3. ○ rack   ○ rake

4. ○ met   ○ meat

5. ○ cap   ○ cape

6. ○ wet   ○ wheat

7. ○ tap   ○ tape

8. ○ man   ○ main

9. ○ set   ○ seat

10. ○ red   ○ reed

Phonics Review
Skill: /ā/, /ă/, /ē/, /ĕ/

Circle the correct word.

1. The man sat in the seat / set .

2. It began to rain / ran .

3. A bee came out of the three / trees .

4. The angry bee / bean stung the man's hand.

5. The sting gave him a sharp pan / pain .

---

6. A humpback well / whale swam in the sea.

7. He needed to get his next mill / meal .

8. He went past a seal / sill .

9. The seal had a fish to eat / each .

10. The whale at / ate many little fish.

Phonics Review
Skill: /ā/ and /ē/

The vowel letter *i* sometimes says its long sound.
Examples: pie, stripe

Name _____

Circle the pictures that have the long *i* sound.

1.

2.

3.

4.

5.

6.

7.

8.

9.

10.

11.

12.

Phonics Review
Skill: /ī/

85

Mark the correct word.

1. ○ slide ○ slip

2. ○ Tim ○ time

3. ○ white ○ wait

4. ○ mile ○ mill

5. ○ smile ○ slim

6. ○ hive ○ have

7. ○ bike ○ back

8. ○ strap ○ stripe

9. ○ dim ○ dime

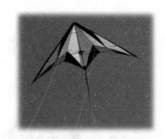

10. ○ kit ○ kite

11. ○ fill ○ file

12. ○ pin ○ pine

Phonics Review
Skill: /ī/ in VCe pattern

Sometimes the long *i* sound is spelled *igh*. The letters *gh* are silent. Examples: sigh, light

Mark the correct word.

1. ○ night   ○ sunlight

2. ○ nighttime   ○ sunlight

3. ○ tight   ○ flight

4. ○ light   ○ high

5. ○ lightning   ○ lightest

6. ○ Dwight   ○ sigh

7. ○ flight   ○ fight

8. ○ lightning   ○ nightlight

9. ○ highway   ○ slight

10. ○ might   ○ midnight

Phonics Review
Skill: *igh* as /ī/

Write each word on the correct board.

bill	bite	chip	dish	five	hide
line	mist	pin	tie	twist	wife

Long _i_

Short _i_

Phonics Review
Skill: /ĭ/ and /ī/

Write the letter of the word that completes
each sentence.

a. hide	b. line	c. ride	d. shines	e. slide

_____ 1. We will play at the park when the sun _____.

_____ 2. I love to go down the _____ at the park.

_____ 3. We will not have to wait in a long _____.

_____ 4. I may play _____-and-seek.

_____ 5. I will _____ my bike home.

a. beside	b. fine	c. mine	d. tide	e. time

_____ 6. I was sick yesterday, but today I feel _____.

_____ 7. I think we can go play _____ the sea.

_____ 8. I like to pick up shells when the _____ is low.

_____ 9. This big shell is _____.

_____ 10. I have such a good _____ at the beach.

Phonics Review
Skill: /ī/

89

Write each word in the correct column.

band	cape	desk	feed	gate	gift
grip	high	jack	jail	keep	kept
left	light	math	pike	slick	team

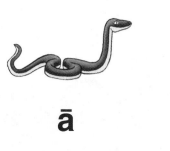

ā

ē

ī

ă

ĕ

ĭ

Phonics Review
Skill: /ă/, /ā/, /ĕ/, /ē/, /ĭ/, /ī/

The vowel letter *o* sometimes says its long sound.
Examples: stone, road

Circle the pictures that have the long *o* sound.

 1.	 2.	 3.
 4.	 5.	 6.
 7.	 8.	 9.
 10.	 11.	 12.

Phonics Review
Skill: /ō/

Write a long-vowel word with a silent *e* to name each picture.

1. _____

2. _____

3. _____

4. _____

5. _____

6. _____

7. _____

8. _____

9. _____

10. _____

Phonics Review
Skill: /ō/ in VCe pattern

When two vowels are together, often the first vowel is long and the second one is silent.
Examples: coal, float

The letter *w* sometimes acts as a vowel. When it comes after the vowel *o*, the letter *w* may act as the silent second vowel.
Examples: grow, blown

| boat | bowl | coat | crow | goat |
| oats | road | snow | soap | toad |

Write the correct word under each picture.

1. _____

2. _____

3. _____

4. _____

5. _____

6. _____

7. _____

8. _____

9. _____

10. _____

Phonics Review
Skill: vowel digraphs *oa*, *ow* as /ō/

Write the word to complete each sentence.

Flo	go	hi	I	Jo
me	no	she	so	we

1. We have _____ pets at home.

2. I would like to have a dog named _____ .

3. _____ have a pet shop near our house.

4. I _____ to the pet shop when I can.

5. That is _____ I can pet the dogs!

6. Miss _____ is the pet shop owner.

7. _____ is nice to me.

8. When I see Miss Jo at the pet shop, she tells me _____ .

9. I am glad she lets _____ pet the dogs.

10. Maybe someday _____ can have a dog.

Phonics Review
Skill: long vowels in open syllables

Mark the correct word.

1. ◯ globe   ◯ glow

2. ◯ moat   ◯ mow

3. ◯ hole   ◯ hose

4. ◯ bow   ◯ bowl

5. ◯ toes   ◯ toast

6. ◯ mole   ◯ mote

7. ◯ yoke   ◯ yo-yo

8. ◯ goal   ◯ grow

9. ◯ float   ◯ flown

10. ◯ tote   ◯ note

Phonics Review
Skill: /ō/

Put a macron or breve over the first vowel in each word.
Use a – to mark a long *o*. Use a ˘ to mark a short *o*.
Use a blue crayon to color the race cars with long *o* words.
Use a red crayon to color the race cars with short *o* words.

nōte

nŏt

1. hole

2. goat

3. rode

4. globe

5. tone

6. block

7. hog

8. sock

9. blow

10. loft

Phonics Review
Skills: /ŏ/, /ō/; breve and macron

Write three rhyming words in the same word family.

Name

1. vine

_____

_____

_____

2. hole

_____

_____

_____

3. she

_____

_____

_____

4. eat

_____

_____

_____

5. hike

_____

_____

_____

6. coat

_____

_____

_____

7. plate

_____

_____

_____

8. rain

_____

_____

_____

9. rose

_____

_____

_____

Phonics Review
Skill: long-vowel rhymes

Circle the correct word.

1. At the petting zoo, Rebecca petted the goat / got .

2. The man helped Esther hop / hope up on the pony.

3. She rode on the pony's bake / back .

4. Watch the bunny rack / rake the straw into a pile.

5. Pet / Pete threw seed to the chickens.

6. He held the pan / pain high away from the goats.

7. Stay out of the pig's slop / slope !

8. Put the pin / pine back in the gate so it will stay shut.

9. We were sad when it was Tim / time to go.

10. Be sure to wash your hands well with stop / soap !

98

Phonics Review
Skill: long and short vowels

Circle the pictures that have the long *u* sound.

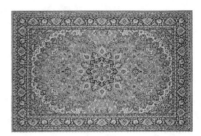

1.

2.

3.

4.

5.

6.

7.

8.

9.

10.

11.

12.

When a word has one vowel followed by one consonant and a final *e*, the first vowel is long and the *e* is silent.
Examples: spruce, mute

Mark the correct word.

When there are two vowels in a word or syllable, often the first vowel says its long sound and the second vowel is silent.
Examples: true, juice

1. ○ moat   ○ suit

2. ○ tune   ○ ten

3. ○ glue   ○ gull

4. ○ June   ○ Jane

5. ○ tube   ○ tub

6. ○ meal   ○ mule

7. ○ cub   ○ cube

8. ○ flute   ○ flat

9. ○ fruit   ○ fun

10. ○ dune   ○ dine

100

Write each word in the correct column.

blue	cube	cute	fruit	glue
hutch	nuts	rule	scrub	spun
strum	truck	trust	tune	

Long _u_

Short _u_

Phonics Review
Skill: /ŭ/, /ū/

Mark the vowel sound for each picture.

1. ○ ā ○ ē ○ ī ○ ō ○ ū

2. ○ ā ○ ē ○ ī ○ ō ○ ū

3. ○ ā ○ ē ○ ī ○ ō ○ ū

9

4. ○ ā ○ ē ○ ī ○ ō ○ ū

5. ○ ā ○ ē ○ ī ○ ō ○ ū

6. ○ ā ○ ē ○ ī ○ ō ○ ū

7. ○ ā ○ ē ○ ī ○ ō ○ ū

8. ○ ā ○ ē ○ ī ○ ō ○ ū

9. ○ ā ○ ē ○ ī ○ ō ○ ū

10. ○ ā ○ ē ○ ī ○ ō ○ ū

11. ○ ā ○ ē ○ ī ○ ō ○ ū

12. ○ ā ○ ē ○ ī ○ ō ○ ū

102

Phonics Review
Skill: review long vowels

Write a long-vowel word with a silent *e* to name each picture.

1.

_____

2.

_____

3.

_____

4.

_____

Write each word in the correct column.

| bike | cube | fresh | pack | pray |
| robe | speak | spill | spun | trot |

Long-vowel words

_____

_____

_____

_____

_____

_____

Short-vowel words

_____

_____

_____

_____

_____

_____

Phonics Review: *Review*
Skill: long and short vowels

Write the word that describes each clue.

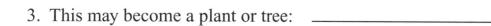

1. You use this to make a pile of leaves: _____

2. You can sail and swim in this: _____

3. This may become a plant or tree: _____

4. Something with two wheels that you ride: _____

5. The number of fingers on each hand: _____

6. Something used to stick two papers together: _____

7. A way to take the skin off an apple: _____

8. Something that must be obeyed: _____

9. A street or path: _____

10. The ten small things on the end of your feet: _____

Phonics Review: *Review*
Skill: long vowels

When the first vowel is followed by one consonant and -*le*, the vowel is usually long.
Example: noble

Write the correct word under each picture.

| Bible | bridle | bugle | cradle | ladle |
| maple | stable | staple | table | title |

1. _____

2. _____

3. _____

4. _____

5. _____

6. _____

7. _____

8. _____

9. _____

10. _____

Phonics Review
Skill: -*le* after long vowels

105

When the first vowel is followed by one consonant and -*le*, the vowel is usually long.
Example: maple

When the first vowel is followed by two consonants and -*le*, the vowel is usually short.
Example: puddle

m ā p l e

p ŭ d d l e

Mark a ˘ over the first vowel if it is short.
Mark a – over the first vowel if it is long.

1. cable

2. tumble

3. crumble

4. fāble

5. riddle

6. settle

7. able

8. freckle

9. noble

10. idle

Phonics Review
Skills: -*le* after long and short vowels; breve and macron

When *y* is at the end of a word or syllable, it acts like a vowel. When it comes after the vowel *a*, the letter *y* acts as the silent second vowel.

Examples: day, play

When it is the only vowel at the end of a one-syllable word, *y* usually says /ī/ as in *try*.

Examples: fly, dry

Mark the correct word.

1. ◯ skip ◯ sky

2. ◯ fly ◯ fight

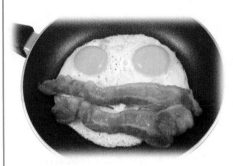

3. ◯ fry ◯ flat

4. ◯ cry ◯ crib

5. ◯ shelf ◯ shy

6. ◯ play ◯ ply

7. ◯ pry ◯ pray

8. ◯ try ◯ tray

9. ◯ spy ◯ spine

Phonics Review
Skill: *y* as /ī/

Circle one word in each sentence that has a *y* that sounds like long *i*.

1. The sky was gray when we got home.

2. Yates said, "I spy a cloud."

3. Everyone had to try to be fast.

4. We did not stay dry on the way inside.

5. That is why the yellow van is still parked at the gate.

6. Your bag is by the back door.

7. Dave, you, and I will fly to Texas.

8. We will see my Uncle Yoshi there.

9. Little Dave may cry on the plane.

10. Dave is very shy.

Phonics Review
Skill: *y* as /ī/

When *y* is at the end of a word or syllable, it acts like a vowel. When it is the only vowel at the end of a word with more than one syllable, *y* usually says /ē/ as in *puppy*.
Examples: happy, funny

Write the letter of the correct clue beside each word.

_____ 1. happy
a. not sad

_____ 2. angry
b. not happy

_____ 3. candy
c. something sweet to eat

_____ 4. empty
d. a young dog

_____ 5. puppy
e. none inside

_____ 6. pansy
f. a coin

_____ 7. hungry
g. a father

_____ 8. penny
h. how you feel if you have not eaten

_____ 9. daddy
i. go fast

_____ 10. quickly
j. a flower

Mark the correct picture.

1. sunny   ◯ ◯

2. fuzzy  ◯ ◯

3. happy   ◯ ◯

4. Mandy   ◯ ◯

5. puppy  ◯ ◯

6. windy  ◯ ◯

Write the correct word under each picture.

bunny	jelly	kitty
sixty	teddy	twenty

7. _____

60

8. _____

9. _____

10. _____

11. _____

20

12. _____

Phonics Review
Skill: *y* as /ē/

Mark *i* or *e* for the sound of *y* in each word.

1. silly   ◯ i   ◯ e

2. shy   ◯ i   ◯ e

3. happy   ◯ i   ◯ e

4. funny   ◯ i   ◯ e

5. fly   ◯ i   ◯ e

6. fry   ◯ i   ◯ e

7. spy   ◯ i   ◯ e

8. try   ◯ i   ◯ e

9. muddy   ◯ i   ◯ e

10. sky   ◯ i   ◯ e

11. sunny   ◯ i   ◯ e

12. rusty   ◯ i   ◯ e

Phonics Review
Skill: *y* as /ī/ and /ē/

Write the word to complete each sentence.

| empty | my | snowy | spy | why |

1. _____ family is going to the zoo!

2. _____ is the elephant in the water?

3. The monkey cage is _____!

4. The _____ owl is very pretty.

5. Do you _____ the python slithering?

| butterfly | by | monkey | rainy | silly |

6. The zookeeper stood _____ the garden as he talked.

7. A _____ landed on the flower beside him.

8. He told a _____ tale about the animals in the zoo.

9. One of the animals was the spider _____.

10. We are glad that it was not _____ for our day at the zoo.

112

A few word families do not follow the rules. Even though the vowel is followed by consonants and no other vowel is present, the vowel is long. Examples: old, grind

Draw a line from the word to the correct picture.

1. bolt
2. colt

3. child
4. wild

5. find
6. rind

7. gold
8. fold
9. mold
10. told

Phonics Review
Skill: long vowels in closed syllables

Write the word to complete each sentence.

bold	child	colt	find	grind
hold	kinds	mind	told	wild

1. When we go to the zoo, we will _____ many

   different animals.

2. Most of the zoo animals are _____.

3. There are other _____ as well.

4. The mare is taking good care of her _____.

5. The zookeeper must _____ up food for the animals

   that are sick.

6. He _____ us some of the things that different animals eat.

7. We were sad that we could not _____ the monkey.

8. One brave _____ offered to hold a snake!

9. The other students were not so _____.

10. Be sure to _____ your manners!

Phonics Review
Skill: long vowels in closed syllables

C says /s/ when it is followed by *e, i,* or *y*.
This kind of *c* is called a *soft c*.
Examples: cent, circus, cycle

C says /k/ when it is followed by *a, o,* or *u*.
This kind of *c* is called a *hard c*.
Examples: cave, coat, circus

C is usually hard when it is followed by a consonant.
Examples: clock, cycle

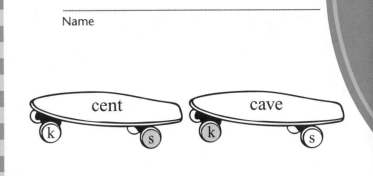

Color the correct wheel for the sound of *c* in each word.

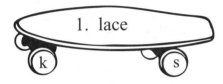
1. lace

2. clap

3. princess

4. fancy

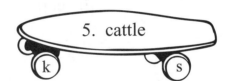
5. cattle

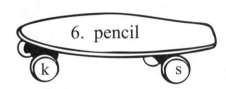
6. pencil

7. cuddle

8. candle

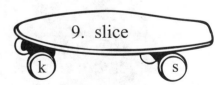
9. slice

10. cake

11. nice

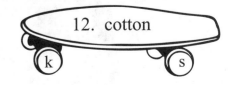
12. cotton

Phonics Review
Skill: hard and soft *c*

115

Mark *k* or *s* for the sound of *c* in each word.

1. can ○ k ○ s

2. celery ○ k ○ s

3. cage ○ k ○ s

4. camel ○ k ○ s

5. city ○ k ○ s

6. mice ○ k ○ s

7. face ○ k ○ s

8. cast ○ k ○ s

9. rice ○ k ○ s

10. cup ○ k ○ s

Phonics Review
Skill: hard and soft *c*

G says /j/ when it is followed by *e, i,* or *y.*
This kind of *g* is called a *soft g.*
Examples: gentle, giraffe, gym

G says /g/ when it is followed by *a, o,* or *u.*
This kind of *g* is called a *hard g.*
Examples: gate, go, gust

G is also hard when it is followed by a consonant or is at the end of a word.
Examples: great, bug

gave	gel	germ	ginger
glide	gold	green	Gus
gust	gym	gypsy	rage
rug	stage		

Write each word in the correct column.

Soft *g*

Hard *g*

_____

_____

_____

_____

_____

_____

_____

_____

_____

_____

_____

_____

_____

_____

_____

_____

_____

_____

Write the correct word under each picture.

1. _____

2. _____

3. _____

4. _____

5. _____

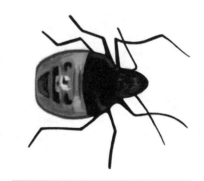

6. _____

7. _____

8. _____

9. _____

Phonics Review
Skill: hard and soft *g*

Mark the correct word.

Name _____

1. ◯ braces   ◯ brakes

2. ◯ Mike   ◯ mice

3. ◯ pickle   ◯ pencil

4. ◯ princess   ◯ pecans

5. ◯ spaceship   ◯ speech

6. ◯ hug   ◯ huge

7. ◯ juggle   ◯ giggle

8. ◯ gym   ◯ gum

9. ◯ hinge   ◯ hang

10. ◯ germ   ◯ gold

11. ◯ squiggle   ◯ cage

12. ◯ fence   ◯ fancy

Phonics Review
Skill: hard and soft *c* and *g*

Write the word to complete each sentence.

| fancy | gentleman | nice | prince | rice |

1. The princess wears a _____ dress.

2. She will go to lunch with the _____.

3. He is a true _____.

4. They will ride in a _____ carriage.

5. They will eat meat with _____ and gravy.

| chance | gently | huge | space | strange |

6. Wes was dreaming that he went into _____.

7. He rode in a _____ rocket.

8. The rocket landed at a _____ place.

9. This was his _____ to explore!

10. Just then, he felt Mom _____ wake him up.

In a few special word families, the letters *ie* can say /ē/.
Example: thief

Write the word to complete each sentence.

brief   chief   field   shield   yield

1. The Scottish _____ led his men in the fight.

2. The men went onto the _____.

3. Each one held his _____.

4. The men had a _____ battle.

5. The brave men did not _____.

believe   brief   niece   piece   shriek

6. Miss Dunn's _____ came to play.

7. She ate a _____ of cake.

8. She gave a _____ when she was tickled.

9. She did not _____ it was time to go home!

10. She said her stay was too _____.

Write each word in the correct column.

/ī/ as in *sky*

/ē/ as in *field*

Phonics Review
Skill: /ē/, /ī/

Two words are sometimes combined to make a new word called a *compound* word.
Examples: goldfish, lunchbox

Write the word to complete each sentence.

| backpack | driveway | forecast |
| rainbow | sunglasses | weekend |

1. We planned a trip for last _____.

2. Friday it rained, but then we saw a _____.

3. Saturday, the _____ was for a sunny day.

4. We ran along the _____ to the car.

5. Dad put his _____ on.

6. Kate had her big red _____.

| anthill | highway | hotdogs |
| sunshine | tablecloth | watermelon |

7. We left to enjoy the _____!

8. We drove west on the _____.

9. We laid the picnic food on a red and white _____.

10. Dad grilled the _____.

11. Mom had _____ for dessert.

12. We ate quickly since we spotted an _____ nearby!

Write the word to complete each sentence.

daytime	peacocks	popcorn	snowdrift	wetlands

1. It was cold at the zoo, even in the _____.

2. The polar bear was lying in a _____.

3. We saw cranes and ducks on the _____.

4. _____ were on the grass beside the path.

5. Dad got us _____ to eat.

butterfly	goldfish	jellyfish	peanut	stingrays

6. Bethanne liked the _____ garden best.

7. We got to see the elephant eat a _____.

8. We liked the _____ in the tanks.

9. Bobby made faces at the _____.

10. We all got to feed the _____.

Phonics Review
Skill: compound words

Add a vowel to make a word with a
long-vowel sound.

Name

1. cut _____

2. pan _____

3. cub _____

4. hop _____

5. rip _____

6. got _____

Write a long-vowel word to name each picture.

7. _____

8. _____

9. _____

10. _____

11. _____

12. _____

Phonics Review
Skill: spelling long-vowel words

Complete the crossword puzzle using the words in the box.

coat	face	flute	guppy
he	hungry	peas	pray
shield	shy	snake	tight

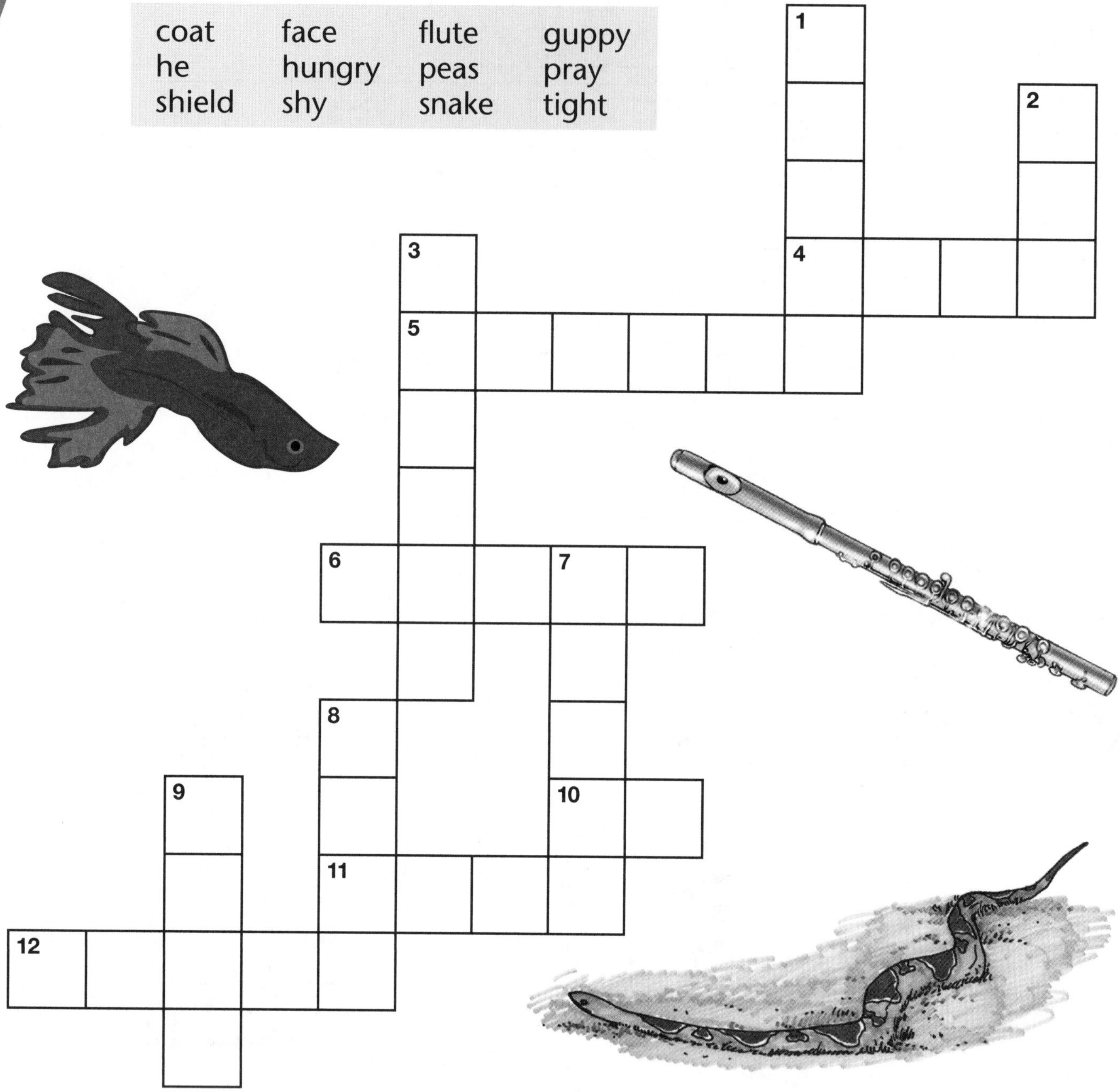

Across

4. speak to God
5. need food
6. a musical instrument
10. pronoun for a man
11. clothing
12. viper

Down

1. a fish
2. timid
3. a piece of armor
7. held fast
8. front of head
9. round green vegetables

Phonics Review
Skill: long-vowel words

Imagine a trip to the zoo.
Write a postcard to a friend to tell about the zoo.
Use the words in the box or your own words to tell about the trip.

giraffe	cage	seal	hay	sunny
mice	field	goats	tires	rain
snakes	feed	eat	day	dry

Phonics Review
Skill: composition

Use the key to color the picture.

| ā red | ē green | ī yellow | ō orange | ū blue |

feet   glue

bugle

treat

lie

rule

eve

by   say

speak

grain

grow

he

fruit

close

load

place

hi

noble

size

tune

go   shriek

make

right

Phonics Review
Skill: reading long-vowel words

Going to the Zoo

God made many kinds of animals. The zoo is a neat place to visit wildlife from other parts of the world. You will see animals that amaze you.

1

The bald eagle is a mighty bird that soars in the sky. When in flight, it can be up to eight feet across from the end of one wing to the end of the other.

It makes nests high in trees or on the side of cliffs. Both the mother and father eagle take care of the nest. There may be one to three eggs. When the eggs hatch, the adults bring fish and meat to feed the baby eaglets. The parents teach the baby eaglets to fly.

Bald eagles are not really bald. The name comes from the white feathers on their heads. The eaglets are fluffy and gray when they hatch. As they grow, they turn brown. They do not grow white feathers until they are adults.

4

You may see a cage with a rattlesnake. Snakes are reptiles. The rattlesnake's skin has dry scales. A rattle grows at the end of the tail.

A rattlesnake hunts at night. It lies in wait to catch small animals. It eats rodents such as mice. Before the snake strikes, its rattle shakes. Its bite has venom that can kill. It may wait two weeks between meals.

When baby snakes are born, they are able to hunt right away.

In the wild, zebras live in the grasslands. At the zoo, you might find them in a field that is like their home on the plains. Zebras graze on grass and shrubs. They may even nibble on small trees.

They have a short mane that is stiff like brush bristles. Zebras have black and white stripes that help them blend into the grass. Their noses are black.

A baby zebra is a foal. The foals stay close to their mothers.

Mark a – over the first vowel if it is long.
Mark a ˘ over the first vowel if it is short.

1. day	2. track
3. crumble	4. rule
5. crow	6. drip
7. he	8. settle
9. wobble	10. sight

Circle the correct word.

11. The snake / rake hissed at the mouse.

12. Tim liked / spiked the python the best.

13. He poked / joked John to scare him.

14. He / Be jumped when the snake lunged at him.

15. There was not enough space / race for the mouse to get away.

16. We were glad that we were on this side / pride of the glass.

17. Nothing could save / gave the mouse now!

18. John was quite / bite glad to leave the reptile house.

Phonics Review: Checkup
Skills: long and short vowels; breve and macron

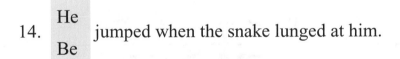

Mark the sound of *c* or *g* in each word.

1. face ○ s ○ k		2. huge ○ j ○ g
3. mice ○ s ○ k		4. got ○ j ○ g
5. cup ○ s ○ k		6. gym ○ j ○ g

Mark the correct word.

7. ○ field ○ feed

8. ○ shield ○ niece

9. ○ cage ○ rage

10. ○ city ○ fuzzy

11. ○ spaceship ○ fireplace

12. ○ rainy ○ sunny

Draw a line to make a compound word.

13. egg	cuffs		16. rain	glasses
14. sun	set		17. sun	box
15. hand	shells		18. sand	bow

Phonics Review: Checkup
Skills: soft and hard *c* and *g*; long vowels; compound words

Unit 4

At the Canyon Rim

Eileen M. Berry

Rock panorama
Spread out at my feet;
Red, gold, and brown tones
Blend as they meet.

Breath drawn in deeply,
Whistled out slow,
At the feeling of looking
So far down below.

To think that God watches
Like this over all
Makes me feel safer
And oh-so-small.

Unit 4 Contents

Long-Vowel Pair /o͞o/ 135–36

Short-Vowel Pair /o͝o/ 137–38

Long and Short *oo* 139–40

Sound of *ew*; Homophones 141–42

r-Influenced Vowel *or* 143–44

r-Influenced Vowel *ar* 145–46

r-Influenced Vowels *er, ir, ur* 147–48

r-Influenced Vowels 149–50

Review 151–52

ost, oth, oft, oss 153

all Sound 154

au and *aw* 155–56

ô Sound 157–58

ou and *ow* 159–62

oi and *oy* 163–64

Composition 165

Review 166

Reading a Story 167–68

Checkup 169–70

When two vowels are together, they may be called a vowel pair. The vowel pair makes one sound that may be different from either of the two vowels.

The vowel pair *oo* sometimes says its long sound, /o͞o/ as in *zoo*.

Name _____

Mark the correct word.

1. ○ noodles   ○ needles

2. ○ stool   ○ stole

3. ○ roots   ○ roof

4. ○ broom   ○ brown

5. ○ boots   ○ boom

6. ○ doom   ○ bamboo

7. ○ groom   ○ goose

8. ○ proof   ○ pool

9. ○ spoon   ○ spin

10. ○ mood   ○ moon

Phonics Review
Skill: *oo* /o͞o/

Write the word to complete each sentence.

hoot	moon	moose	mushrooms	pool

1. The _____ ran into the forest.

2. Something in the trees went _____.

3. The _____ shone brightly.

4. A moth settled on some _____.

5. The moose rested beside a _____.

bedroom	caboose	food	noon	toot

6. Wes and Beth left on the train at _____.

7. The engine gave a long _____.

8. The dining car had _____ for everyone.

9. The sleeper car was like a _____.

10. The _____ was the last car on the train.

Phonics Review
Skill: oo /ōo/

The vowel pair *oo* sometimes says its short sound, /o͝o/ as in *book*.

Name _____

Write the correct word with *book* to name each picture.

bookbag	bookends	bookmark	bookshelf	bookstore
checkbook	cookbook	notebook	scrapbook	textbook

1. _____

2. _____

3. _____

4. _____

5. _____

6. _____

7. _____

8. _____

9. _____

10. _____

Phonics Review
Skill: *oo* /o͝o/

Write the word to complete each sentence.

| football | good | looked | stood | took |

1. The team _____ on the field.

2. The team's plan was _____.

3. The quarterback _____ his place.

4. He _____ behind him.

5. He was going to pass the _____!

| brook | hook | hooves | woof | wool |

6. The horse has four _____.

7. The sheep give us _____.

8. The farmer's dog said, "_____."

9. The farmer went to the _____.

10. He got a fish on his _____.

Phonics Review
Skill: *oo* /o͞o/

Write the long *oo* /o͞o/ words under the hoop.
Write the short *oo* /o͝o/ words under the fishhook.

bamboo	bloom	bookmark	booth
brook	checkbook	cool	foot
good	moonlight	room	spoon
stood	took	toothbrush	wood

Long *oo*

Short *oo*

Phonics Review
Skill: long and short *oo*

Write the word to complete each sentence.

bedroom   broom   firewood   footstools   wooden

1. Grandpa got some _____ for the chilly evening.

2. Grandma sent Hal for the _____ to sweep the mess.

3. Hal swept the _____ floor.

4. Then Hal went into his _____ to rest.

5. Grandma and Grandpa both rested their feet on _____.

goose   look   noon   shook   tool

6. On Christmas Day we opened our presents before _____.

7. Tom gave Dad a new _____ for his garage.

8. Grandpa got a fake _____ to put on the lawn.

9. _____ at Mom's pretty necklace!

10. Sarah _____ her new piggy bank to look for money.

Phonics Review
Skill: long and short *oo*

The vowel pair *ew* may say /ōō/ or /yōō/.
Examples: new, few

Name _____

Write the correct word under each picture.

| chew | crew | drew | jewels | screws | stew |

1. _____

2. _____

3. _____

4. _____

5. _____

6. _____

Circle the homophone for each sentence that makes the most sense. You may use your dictionary.

Homophones are words that sound the same but have different spellings and meanings.
Example: hew, hue

7. John was sick with the flu / flew .

8. The bird flu / flew to its nest.

9. Anna and Elly blue / blew bubbles outside.

10. Today the sky is quite blue / blew .

11. The grass is sparkling with the due / dew .

12. Mom will pay the bill that is due / dew .

Phonics Review
Skills: letter-sound association *ew* /ōō/; homophones

Complete the crossword puzzle using the words in the box.

| chew | crews | dew | flew | jewels |
| new | news | screws | stew | threw |

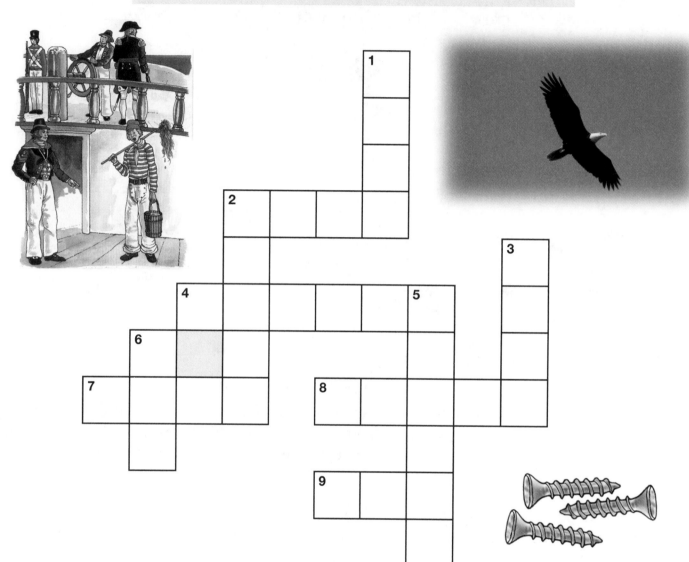

Across

2. to grind, crunch, or gnaw with teeth
4. gems
7. information about events
8. opposite of *caught*
9. opposite of *old*

Down

1. how the bird got to the nest
2. groups that work together
3. a pot of soup
5. these hold two things together
6. small drops of water

Phonics Review
Skill: *ew* /ōō/

When *r* follows a vowel, it influences the vowel's sound.
Usually *or* says /ôr/ as in *horn*.

Mark the correct word.

1. ◯ corn   ◯ core | 2. ◯ mare   ◯ more | 3. ◯ horse   ◯ hose

Write the word to complete each sentence.

cord	explore	forms
north	record	worn

4. At the Grand Canyon you can _____.

5. In the canyon you will see the _____ of rocks that God has made.

6. The rocks were _____ by wind and water.

7. You may want to follow the path going _____.

8. Strap all your things to a mule with a _____.

9. Be sure to _____ all that you see and do.

Circle the correct word.

1. Christopher Columbus was **born** / corn in 1451.

2. He became a **explore** / sailor at the age of fourteen.

3. Columbus loved to **explore** / border .

4. Some people thought that the earth was flat and **sort** / short .

5. They thought he would sail off the **corner** / core of the earth.

6. Three ships left the **core** / harbor to sail across the ocean.

7. Columbus had to find out which way was **north** / shore .

8. People were happy when he sailed back into **horn** / port .

9. Later Columbus took **more** / snore trips.

10. What Columbus did has not been **forgotten** / order .

144

Name _____

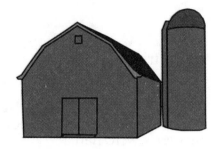

bark	barn	car	cart	farm
farmer	garden	stars	start	tar

Write the word that matches each definition.

_____ 1. short, gruff sound made by a dog

_____ 2. a large piece of land for crops and animals

_____ 3. a wooden object with wheels that can be pulled by an animal

_____ 4. a person who plants crops and cares for animals

_____ 5. to begin an action

_____ 6. a small piece of land for flowers or vegetables

_____ 7. thick, sticky, dark material used for roads

_____ 8. a large farm building used for animals

_____ 9. something to take a ride in

_____ 10. bright lights in the night sky

Circle the correct word.

1. We took a trip to a **farm / shark** .

2. The farmer's wife had a **barber / cart** full of apples.

3. She was going to make **tarts / tarps** .

4. We saw some vegetables in the smaller **pardon / garden** .

5. We ate our apple treat outside in the **yard / lark** .

6. Mom **sharpened / parked** the car in the cleaner's parking lot.

7. The cleaners will **lark / starch** Dad's white shirts.

8. They will also clean Susie's **scarf / spark** .

9. They will get the black **mark / smart** out.

10. Fido, our dog, **charmed / barked** from the car.

146

Usually *er*, *ir*, and *ur* say /ûr/ as in *her*, *bird*, and *nurse*.

Name _____

Write the correct word under each picture.

bird	burn	fern	girl
herd	nurse	purple	purse
shirt	skirt	turtle	verse

1. _____

2. _____

3. _____

4. _____

5. _____

6. _____

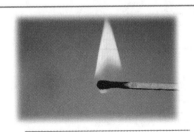

7. _____

8. _____

9. _____

10. _____

11. _____

12. _____

Phonics Review
Skill: *er*, *ir*, and *ur* as /ûr/

Write the word to complete each sentence.

banner	members	perform	purple	verses

1. The _____ of our church are giving a program.

2. Tom and Frank will make a large _____ .

3. The letters will be written in _____ .

4. Our singers will _____ a new song.

5. Pastor Murr will read many _____ from the Bible.

curb	Curt	her	teacher	turned

6. Lisa _____ left on the next street.

7. She was on the way to _____ uncle's home.

8. She stepped off the _____ and crossed the street.

9. Uncle _____ was going to help her study.

10. He is a math _____ .

148

Write the two correct words beside each picture.
Choose one word from each box for each picture.

Name

| curly | dirty | furry | orange | | corn | fern | scarf | shirt |
| purple | sparkling | torn | warm | | skirt | squirrel | star | turtle |

1. _____   _____

2. _____   _____

3. _____   _____

4. _____   _____

5. _____   _____

6. _____   _____

7. _____   _____

8. _____   _____

Phonics Review
Skill: *ar, or, ur*

Write the word to complete each sentence.

| barked | bird | dirty | for | over |
| perched | shirt | tore | wore | yard |

1. One day I was wearing my purple _____ .

2. I didn't want to get it _____ .

3. I was playing in the _____with my dog, Skip.

4. A _____ flew by and wanted to play.

5. Skip _____ at the bird.

6. The bird _____ on a tree.

7. Skip jumped _____ the fence to reach it.

8. I grabbed Skip, and my shirt _____ on the fence!

9. Mom was able to mend it _____ me.

10. It wasn't long before I _____ it again.

150

Phonics Review
Skill: *ar, er, ir, or*

Write the word to complete each sentence.

arm	better	hard	hurt	nurse

1. Billy threw the baseball _____.

2. When Jim swung the bat, he got _____.

3. He said there was pain in his _____.

4. The _____ put his arm in a sling.

5. She said it would be _____ in four days.

Cory	fir	first	runners	sore

6. _____ ran in the big race.

7. He wanted to get _____ place.

8. The finish line was at the big _____ tree.

9. He was faster than the other _____.

10. The next day, he was _____ but very happy.

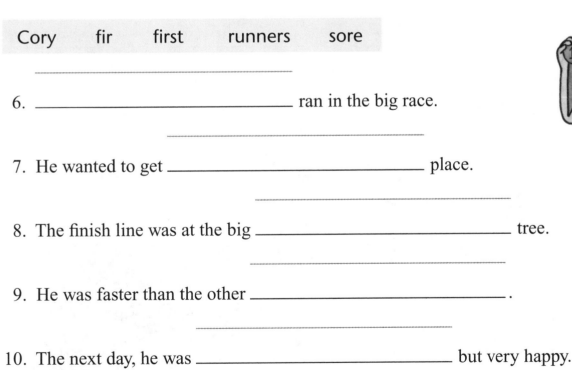

Write each word in the correct column.

| blue | foot | good | hood |
| look | moose | screw | spoon |

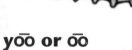

yōo or ōo

ŏŏ

_____

_____

_____

_____

_____

_____

_____

_____

Draw a line from the clue to the correct word.

1. a farm animal   cook

2. a kind of food   crew

3. one who fixes food   fishhook

4. a group of people   rooster

5. used to catch fish   spool

6. holds string   stew

Phonics Review: *Review*
Skill: *ew, oo, ue*

When *o* is followed by *ss*, *st*, *th*, or *ft*, it may say /ô/.
Examples: loss, lost, moth, soft

Write the correct word under each picture.

| cloth | cross | frost | loft | moth | toss |

1. _____

2. _____

3. _____

4. _____

5. _____

6. _____

Mark the word that does **not** rhyme.

7. ◯ broth   ◯ moth   ◯ birth   ◯ cloth

8. ◯ cost   ◯ past   ◯ frost   ◯ lost

9. ◯ dress   ◯ cross   ◯ toss   ◯ boss

10. ◯ loft   ◯ soft   ◯ sift

Phonics Review
Skill: *ost, oth, oft, oss* as /ô/

153

Mark the correct word.

1. ○ small   ○ smile

2. ○ tall   ○ tail

3. ○ footsteps   ○ football

4. ○ mole   ○ mall

5. ○ still   ○ stall

6. ○ hallway   ○ halter

Write the word to complete each sentence.

| all | ball | ballpark | baseball | called |

7. The boys were _____ friends.

8. Tim _____ the others.

9. They decided to go to the _____ .

10. Jimmy threw a _____ .

11. The boys loved _____ .

154

Phonics Review
Skill: *all* sound

> The vowel pairs *au* and *aw* say /ô/.
> Examples: faucet, draw

Name _____

Mark the correct word.

1. ○ sauce   ○ slice

2. ○ lawn   ○ lay

3. ○ stray   ○ straw

4. ○ clay   ○ claw

5. ○ jaws   ○ jewels

6. ○ sway   ○ saw

Write the word to complete each sentence.

| claws | hawk | paw | saw | straw |

7. The farmer _____ his dog coming from the bushes.

8. He sat down on a bale of _____ and looked around.

9. A _____ was flying in the sky.

10. It was too far away to see its _____ .

11. The dog lifted its sore _____ so the farmer could see it.

Write the letter of the definition that matches each word.

_____ 1. lawn   a. an area of ground planted with grass

_____ 2. claw   b. to make a picture

_____ 3. straw   c. a sharp curved nail on the toe of an animal

_____ 4. draw   d. a narrow tube for drinking

_____ 5. saw   a. to cry loudly

_____ 6. jaw   b. a tool with a thin metal blade

_____ 7. bawl   c. bone in the mouth

_____ 8. seesaw   d. long plank with a support in the middle

_____ 9. yawn   a. a name for a boy or man

_____ 10. Paul   b. liquid dressing served on top of another food

_____ 11. fault   c. to open the mouth wide and breathe in deeply

_____ 12. sauce   d. weakness or mistake

Phonics Review
Skill: *aw, au* /ô/

Write the word that matches each phrase.

| boss | call | cost | lost | small | soft |

_____

1. _____   very little

2. _____   the price of an object

3. _____   to speak to someone far away

4. _____   not hard

5. _____   what you cannot find

6. _____   the person in charge

Write two rhyming words in the same word family.

7. all

_____

_____

8. saw

_____

_____

9. loss

_____

_____

10. fawn

_____

_____

Phonics Review
Skill: letter-sound association for /ô/

Mark the sentence that matches the picture.

1.
  ◯ Troy and Brent had fun on the seesaw.

  ◯ Kim and Patty like to draw with colorful markers.

2.
  ◯ The squawking could be heard all around the zoo.

  ◯ The fawn was only about ten yards from our car.

3.
  ◯ It took Dad two hours to cut Grandma's lawn.

  ◯ We got up early enough to enjoy the dawn of a new day.

August

S	M	T	W	TH	F	S
		1	2	3	4	5
6	7	8	9	10	11	12
13	14	15	16	17	18	19
20	21	22	23	24	25	26
27	28	29	30	31		

4.
  ◯ I can't come because I hurt my foot.

  ◯ My birthday is in August.

5.
  ◯ Robin has just learned how to crawl.

  ◯ I'm so tired that it's impossible not to yawn.

6.
  ◯ Joe can draw animals very well.

  ◯ I love chocolate sauce on my ice cream.

Phonics Review
Skill: reading *aw, au* as /ô/

The vowel pairs *ou* and *ow* often say /ou/.
Examples: towel, mouse

Mark the correct word.

1. ○ flour   ○ hour

2. ○ sour   ○ sow

3. ○ growl   ○ ground

4. ○ tore   ○ tower

5. ○ brown   ○ born

6. ○ howl   ○ hole

7. ○ plow   ○ shout

8. ○ town   ○ tower

9. ○ hound   ○ house

10. ○ shower   ○ flower

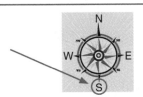

11. ○ sound   ○ south

12. ○ towel   ○ wow

Write the correct word under each picture.
Write two rhyming words in the same word family.

| cloud | clown | cow | mouse | round | shower |

1. _____

2. _____

3. _____

4. _____

5. _____

6. _____

Phonics Review
Skill: *ow, ou* /ow/

Complete the crossword puzzle using the words in the box.

brown	cloud	crown	down
flowers	gown	growl	mouse
owl	towel	town	

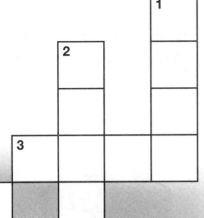

Across

3. what a bride wears
6. an animal that hoots
7. found in a garden
8. worn by a king
9. a small animal
10. where the sun "goes" at the end of the day

Down

1. where people live
2. the sound of an angry dog
4. used to dry dishes
5. a color word
8. found in the sky

Phonics Review
Skill: *ow, ou* /ow/

Write each word in the correct column.

| blow | bowl | brow | clown | crow | crowd | frown |
| low | own | power | show | throw | towel | tower |

ow says ō

ow says /ow/

Phonics Review
Skill: *ow* /ō/ and /ou/

The vowel pairs *oi* and *oy* say /oi/.
Examples: oil, boy

Draw a line from the word to the correct picture.

1. boy

2. toy

3. foil

4. oyster

5. cowboy

6. oil

7. coil

8. coins

9. boil

10. oink

11. point

12. noise

Write the word to complete each sentence.

loyal	moist	poison	royal

1. The _____ family lived in the castle.

2. The king had _____ men to serve him.

3. Servants checked his meals to make sure there was no _____ .

4. They gave the king _____ cloths to clean his hands.

choice	join	soil	spoil	toil	Troy

5. _____ lives in a little house.

6. He has to plow the _____ on his farm.

7. In summer the farmers _____ until sunset.

8. After dark, they _____ the family for dinner.

9. Troy eats all his food so it will not _____ .

10. Then he makes a _____ to play a game or sleep.

Phonics Review
Skill: *oy, oi* /oi/

Imagine that you have gone camping with your best friend's family. Write about what you would do. Use the words in the box or your own words to write about your trip.

few	grew	all	awe	boy
enjoy	choice	cross	ground	haul
stood	hoot	join	voice	lost
noises	owl	small	point	round

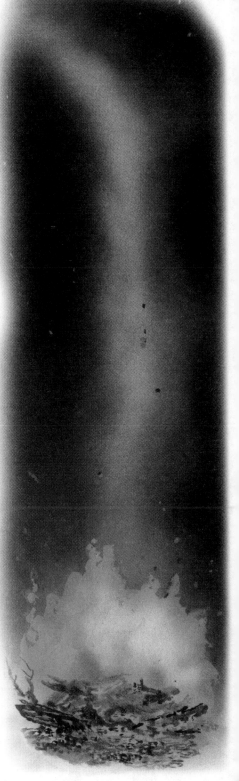

Phonics Review
Skill: composition

165

Write the two correct words beside each picture.
Choose one word from each box for each picture.

| blue | bouncy | cool | | ball | fawn | girl |
| soft | smart | toy | | mouse | owl | shark |

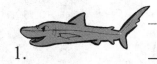

1. _____ _____

2. _____ _____

3. _____ _____

4. _____ _____

5. _____ _____

6. _____ _____

Write a word with *ar* to complete each sentence.

7. A cat mews, but a dog _____ .

8. My uncle can fly a plane, but my dad drives a
_____
_____ .

Phonics Review: *Review*
Skill: special vowel sounds

As the Harpers drove home, Dad spoke of what they had seen. God made these places. He used water from Noah's Flood to carve out the canyon and change the logs to stone. He made the colors in the sand and rocks. The Harpers thanked God for what they had seen.

8

Martha J. Smith - booklet page 5
U.S. Geological Survey - booklet page 6
Tom Berg - booklet page 7

Arizona Parks

The Harpers had come a long way. Cora, Peter, and Joyce were glad it was not much farther. They were all tired. At last, Mom saw the sign for the Grand Canyon.

1

The next day they drove to a forest of stone. In Noah's Flood, water and mud quickly covered the trees. The logs turned to stone. Cora did not pick up any of the stone bark. She left it there for others to see.

6

Peter saw a little fawn back at the cabin. It came out of the woods. It ran when he pointed to it. In the dark that night, something made soft noises. Dad checked the fireplace.

3

They stayed in a small cabin at the park. First they unpacked the van. Then they took a shuttle bus to explore the South Rim. They saw the sunset over the canyon. The sky was red and orange.

2

Close by was a rainbow of sand. It was a place called the Painted Desert. The sand was layered in lots of colors. Some spots were red, orange, and pink. Some were blue, gray, and purple.

7

A small owl had fallen down the chimney. Dad covered it with a blanket. He scooped it up. He took it outside and let it go. For a few moments it just sat and looked around. It gave a short hoot. Then it flew off into the woods.

4

In the morning they explored the park. They looked out at the huge canyon. The layers of rock were red, orange, and brown. Joyce saw a burro on a steep path down below.

5

Circle the correct word.

1. The Grand Canyon is a park / mark .

2. Major Powell and his men went to explore / corner it.

3. They traveled along the Colorado River / Rover .

4. The trip was long and hard, and some men turned / trained back.

5. In 1901 a railroad made the trip to the canyon shorter / sport than before.

6. Today many people enjoy / employ visiting the canyon.

ball	cost	haul
hawk	moth	oil
point	royal	straw

Write the correct word under each picture.

7. _____

8. _____

9. _____

10. _____

11. _____

12. _____

13. _____

14. _____

15. _____

Phonics Review: *Checkup*
Skills: vowel pairs; r-influenced vowels; ô sound

Write the word to complete each sentence.

books	Drew	food
good	grew	look
new	soon	too

1. _____ has a baby brother named John.

2. I think Drew _____ three inches last year.

3. The baby will grow _____ .

4. He likes to try new _____ .

5. He will crawl _____ .

6. Drew is a _____ helper.

7. He likes to _____ for toys for John.

8. Drew gave John a _____ toy.

9. He shows him lots of good _____ .

Write two rhyming words in the same word family.

10. blouse

11. crown

12. flower

Phonics Review: Checkup
Skill: *oo, ew, ow, ou*

Unit 5

Washington, DC

Eileen M. Berry

Capital city we mark with a star,
Place where our memories and monuments are;
Bustling with tourists and traffic and trains,
Cherry trees blooming in parks and on lanes.

Here you can walk around Capitol Hill,
Watch Congress voting on this or that bill,
Listen to justices hearing their cases,
Wait for brief glimpses of notable faces.

Take a quick tour of the President's home,
Photograph building and tower and dome,
Galleries, libraries—stroll right on through.
Visit museums and even the zoo!

City with heritage, city with heart,
City where citizens all share a part.
See all the flags—for our freedom they stand!
God by His grace has protected our land.

Unit 5 Contents

Syllables 173–74

Adding -s or -es 175–80

Base Words and Suffixes 181

Adding -ing 182

Sounds of Suffix -ed 183–84

Adding -ed or -ing 185–86

Adding -ed or -ing to Short-Vowel Words 187

Adding -ed to Short-Vowel Words 188

Adding -ing to Short-Vowel Words 189

Adding -ed or -ing to Short-Vowel Words 190

Suffixes -er and -est 191–92

Suffix -er 193

Suffixes -er and -est 194

Review 195–96

Adding -ed or -es to Words Ending in y 197

Adding -es or -s to Words Ending in y 198

Adding -er or -est to Words Ending in y 199

Adding -es or -s to Words Ending in y 200

Reading Words with -ed or -ing 201–2

Adding -ed or -ing to Long-Vowel Words 203

Adding -ed or -ing to Short- and Long-Vowel Words ... 204

Suffix -ly 205

Suffix -ful 206

Suffixes -less and -ness 207

Suffixes 208

Prefixes re- and a- 209

Prefixes un- and dis- 210

Composition 211–12

Reading a Story 213–14

Checkup 215–16

Words have one or more parts or syllables.
Each syllable has one vowel sound.
Sun has one vowel sound, /ŭ/, so it has one syllable.
Sunshine has two vowel sounds, /ŭ/ and /ī/, so it has two syllables.

Name _____

Say each word. Count the parts.
Circle the number of syllables.

1. storm	1	2		2. house	1	2
3. baggy	1	2		4. handcuff	1	2
5. buzz	1	2		6. windmill	1	2
7. Friday	1	2		8. hillside	1	2
9. treat	1	2		10. floor	1	2
11. toothbrush	1	2		12. seesaw	1	2
13. cook	1	2		14. spice	1	2
15. silk	1	2		16. himself	1	2
17. wait	1	2		18. lift	1	2
19. sandbox	1	2		20. mess	1	2

Phonics Review
Skill: syllables

Say each word. Write the one-syllable words in the column with one coal car. Write the two-syllable words in the column with two coal cars.

| blindfold | boot | cent | chirp | float | football |
| snow | starlight | streetcar | tomcat | train | traintrack |

One-syllable words

Two-syllable words

Phonics Review
Skill: syllables

A suffix is an ending that is added to a word. The suffix *-s* may be added to naming words (nouns) to show more than one. Words that show more than one are plural.
Example: ball, balls

Mark the correct word to match each picture.
Choose the plural if more than one item is pictured.

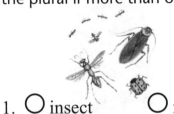

1. ◯ insect   ◯ insects

2. ◯ truck   ◯ trucks

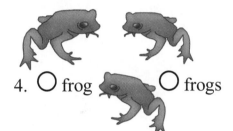

3. ◯ rocket   ◯ rockets

4. ◯ frog   ◯ frogs

The suffix *-es* may be added to nouns that end in *x*, *ss*, *sh*, or *ch* to make them plural.
Example: glass, glasses

5. ◯ dress   ◯ dresses

6. ◯ peach   ◯ peaches

7. ◯ fox   ◯ foxes

8. ◯ finch   ◯ finches

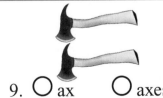

9. ◯ ax   ◯ axes

10. ◯ brush   ◯ brushes

Phonics Review
Skill: adding *-s* or *-es*

When the suffix -*s* is added to a word, the number of syllables does not change.
Example: crow, crows

When the suffix -*es* is added to a word, another syllable is usually added.
Example: patch, patches (patch•es)

Count the syllables and write the number for each word.

1. book _____   books _____   2. lunch _____   lunches _____

3. skateboard _____   skateboards _____   4. fish _____   fishes _____

5. train _____   trains _____   6. paintbrush _____   paintbrushes _____

7. kitten _____   kittens _____   8. sandwich _____   sandwiches _____

Circle the number of syllables for each colored word.

9. How many **stars** are in the sky?   1   2

10. There are twelve **branches** on that tree.   1   2

11. We need two more **boxes** for the apples.   1   2

12. Two **boys** can climb the tree.   1   2

13. We need to trim three more **bushes**.   1   2

Phonics Review
Skill: adding -*s* or -*es*

Add the suffix -s or -es to each word to make each word plural.

Name

Mom's Grocery List

4 peach_____

2 dozen egg_____

2 bar_____ of soap

3 can_____ of peanuts

4 bunch_____ of grapes

Dad's Supply List

5 light bulb_____

2 boxes of nail_____

2 bucket_____ of sand

2 tire patch_____

3 cloth_____

Art Teacher's List

10 colored pencil_____

8 small brush_____

3 bottle_____ of glitter

2 box_____ of paper

6 block_____ of clay

Child's School Supply List

2 glue stick_____

4 book_____

8 crayon_____

2 pack_____ of paper

2 red pen_____

Write the word to complete each sentence.
Add the suffix -s or -es.

| brush | bucket | bush | church | glove |

1. The men plan to clean the steeples at three _____ .

2. They use _____ to protect their hands.

3. They put hot, soapy water in their _____ .

4. They use fine _____ for this job.

5. One brush fell into some _____ .

| flute | fox | princess | room | torch |

6. Three _____ went for a stroll.

7. The path was lit with _____ .

8. Two _____ crossed their path.

9. Some _____ made music.

10. The princesses went back to their _____ in the palace.

Phonics Review
Skill: adding -s or -es

The suffix *-s* or *-es* is added to an action word or verb to change the word. The noun and verb must fit together.
Examples:
Many lions *roar*, but one lion *roars*.
Many men *preach*, but one man *preaches*.

Write the word to complete each sentence. Add the suffix *-s* or *-es*.

buzz	fish
mix	pinch

1. A bee _____.

2. A crab _____.

3. A raccoon _____.

4. A cook _____.

hiss	hop
play	run

5. A snake _____.

6. A bunny _____.

7. A fox _____.

8. A child _____.

chew	chirp
preach	swim

9. A fish _____.

10. A robin _____.

11. A beaver _____.

12. A pastor _____.

Phonics Review
Skill: adding *-s* or *-es*

179

Write the word to complete each sentence.

cleans	cuts	eats	fizzes	messes

_____

1. Zack _____ his lunch.

_____

2. He _____ his sandwich.

_____

3. The drink in his can _____ .

_____

4. He _____ up three napkins.

_____

5. He _____ his spot well.

enjoys	fixes	reaches	visits	wishes

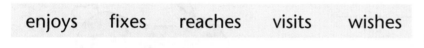

_____

6. Sue _____ a snack to take for her trip.

_____

7. She _____ many places in the city.

_____

8. She _____ the subway.

_____

9. At last she _____ the end of the ride.

_____

10. She _____ that her trip had been longer.

Phonics Review
Skill: adding -s or -es

A base word is a word to which something
is added that will change the word.
Example: camp, camps, camped, camping

Name

Underline the base word. Circle the suffix.

1. locking

2. splashed

3. dusting

4. cleans

5. waited

6. praying

Mark the correct word.

7. We saw a large ___ of Abe Lincoln. ○ paint ○ painting

8. His wife and ___ were with him. ○ son ○ sons

9. They were ___ at a book. ○ looking ○ look

10. The artist had ___ their picture. ○ paint ○ painted

Write the word to complete each sentence.

buzzing	fixing	helping
looking	reading	

1. The bee was _____ around the boy.

2. A man on a park bench was _____ .

3. The family was _____ at a statue of Abe Lincoln.

4. A man was _____ the first lady out of the car.

5. The cook was _____ food for a dinner.

Write the word to complete each sentence. Add the suffix *-ing*.

hold	jump	march	paint	twirl

6. A lady was _____ a camera.

7. The worker was _____ a sign.

8. A band was _____ down the street.

9. John and Zack were _____ up and down.

10. Kim was _____ around in circles.

Phonics Review
Skill: adding *-ing*

The suffix *-ed* may be added to a base word. The suffix *-ed* makes the sound of /t/ as in *pitched*, /d/ as in *played*, or /ed/ as in *waited (wait•ed)*. When the suffix says /ed/, another syllable is added.

Mark the sound the suffix *-ed* makes in each word.

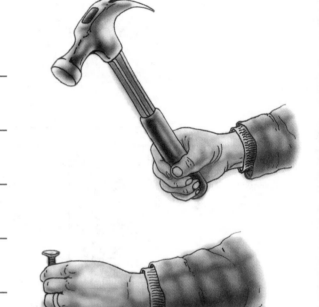

1. docked   ○ t   ○ d   ○ ed

2. called   ○ t   ○ d   ○ ed

3. pounded   ○ t   ○ d   ○ ed

4. fizzed   ○ t   ○ d   ○ ed

5. splashed   ○ t   ○ d   ○ ed

6. picked   ○ t   ○ d   ○ ed

Count the syllables and write the number for each word.

7. printed   _____

8. drilled   _____

9. stacked   _____

10. landed   _____

11. jumped   _____

12. blended   _____

Phonics Review
Skill: /d/, /t/, and /ed/ sounds of suffix *-ed*

Write the correct word under each picture.

| crawled | jumped | painted | planted |

1. _____

2. _____

3. _____

4. _____

Write the word to complete each phrase.

On our vacation we . . .

5. _____ a suitcase.

6. _____ for our team.

7. _____ from the dock.

8. _____ a flat tire.

9. _____ some roses.

10. _____ a ball.

cheered

fished

fixed

packed

smelled

tossed

Phonics Review
Skill: /t/, /d/, and /ed/ sounds of suffix -ed

Circle the correct word.

1. When Adam **bumped** / docked the table, the vase fell off.

2. Mom **locked** / mixed the house before she got in the car.

3. Dad clucked / **dipped** his cookie in the chocolate milk.

4. Grandma **cracked** / dusted nuts for the cookies she made.

5. We flocked / **finished** our homework before we played.

6. Eric **jumped** / helped out of bed and dressed quickly.

7. The students stomped / **clapped** their hands when the band played.

8. The goose started kissing / **hissing** when we got near its nest.

9. My homework paper is **missing** / misses .

10. We **thanked** / splashed the teacher for helping us.

Write the word to complete each sentence.

United States Capitol at night

| meeting | pulled | sparkling |
| traveled | waited | |

1. We _____ to Washington, DC, at night.

2. The train _____ into the city quite late.

3. The Capitol dome was _____ with lights.

4. We _____ outside the next morning.

5. Congress was _____ inside.

| enjoyed | looking | painting | sounded | speaking |

6. One man was _____ to the others.

7. There were many people _____ from upstairs.

8. Inside the dome we saw a man _____ .

9. Our steps _____ loud in the big room.

10. We _____ our trip to the capital city.

Phonics Review
Skill: adding -ed or -ing

When a word has one vowel and two consonants before the suffix, the first vowel is usually short.
Examples: jŭmping, fĭshed

Circle the two consonants before the suffix.
Add a breve (˘) over the first vowel.

1. dusted   2. stamped   3. resting

When a short-vowel word ends in a single consonant, usually the consonant is doubled before adding a suffix that begins with a vowel.
Example: clap, claps, clapped, clapping

Underline the base word. Circle the extra consonant that was added.

4. running   5. stepping   6. batting

Write each base word with the suffixes *-ed* and *-ing*.

7. bless   _____   _____

8. plot   _____   _____

9. grip   _____   _____

10. scrub   _____   _____

Write the word to complete each sentence.
Double the consonant and add the suffix *-ed* to each base word.

dip	nap	sin	stop	strum

1. Adam and Eve _____ in the Garden of Eden.

2. God _____ the army of Egypt at the Red Sea.

3. David _____ his harp.

4. Naaman _____ in the Jordan River.

5. Jonah _____ in a big storm.

bat	drop	flap	grab	pop

6. A flag _____ in the wind.

7. Dad _____ the top from his soda can.

8. The first player _____ the ball.

9. Marta _____ her ice-cream cone.

10. Mom _____ the napkins.

Phonics Review
Skill: adding *-ed* to short-vowel words

Write the word to complete each caption. Double the consonant and add the suffix *-ing* to each base word. Draw a line from the caption to the correct picture.

Name

| bat | clap | dip | fit | grab |

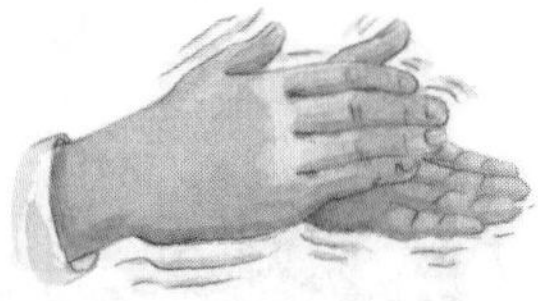

1. _____ cage

2. _____ a cone

3. _____ a bubble

4. _____ a puzzle piece

5. _____ hands

| dig | mop | sit | slip | tap |

6. _____ a floor

7. _____ on the ice

8. _____ on the nail

9. _____ on a nest

10. _____ a hole

Phonics Review
Skill: adding *-ing* to short-vowel words

Circle the correct word.

1. The mother panda was napping / tagging with her cub.

2. We sipped / snapped a picture of them sleeping.

3. The mother woke up and tripped / hugged her baby.

4. She trotted / trimmed over to the water to have a drink.

5. She was tapping / dipping her paw into the cold water as she drank.

6. Then she tapped / snipped some bamboo with her sharp teeth.

7. Her cub awoke as she plopped / petted down beside it.

8. She was patting / chatting the baby when we left.

9. They spotted / trotted us looking at them.

10. Mother panda will not be dipped / robbed of her cub.

190

Phonics Review
Skill: adding -ed or -ing to short-vowel words

The suffix *-er* may be added to a base word to compare two things.
The suffix *-est* may be added to compare more than two things.
Example: short, short*er*, short*est*

Name _____

a small mouse

a smaller mouse

the smallest mouse

Draw a picture to illustrate each phrase.

1.   a tall tree   a taller tree   the tallest tree

2.   a long snake   a longer snake   the longest snake

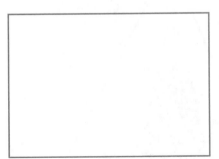

3.   a big dog   a bigger dog   the biggest dog

Phonics Review
Skill: suffixes *-er* and *-est*

Circle the correct word.

1. The Whites' tent is **bigger** / biggest than the Moores' tent.

2. The Franks' tent is the **larger** / largest tent of all.

3. Samuel's flashlight is **brighter** / brightest than Joshua's flashlight.

4. The nearby stream is **colder** / coldest than the pond.

5. My fishing pole is **newer** / newest than Samuel's fishing pole.

6. John caught the **smaller** / smallest fish of all.

7. Today is **hotter** / hottest than yesterday was.

8. John ate his fish **faster** / fastest than I ate mine.

9. My air mattress is the **softer** / softest of all our air mattresses.

10. I slept **longer** / longest than my sister.

big

bigger

bigger

biggest

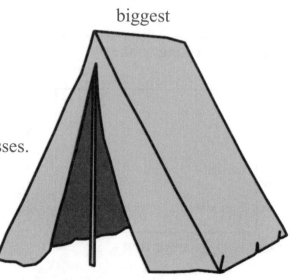

Phonics Review
Skill: suffixes *-er* and *-est*

The suffix *-er* may be added to some action verbs to change them to nouns.
Example: catch, catcher

Write the correct word under each picture.

jumper	kicker	marker
painter	reader	singer
speaker	stinger	teacher

1. _____

2. _____

3. _____

4. _____

5. _____

6. _____

7. _____

8. _____

9. _____

If the base word has a short vowel and one consonant, the consonant is doubled before adding the suffix *-er*.
Example: sit, sitter

| batter |
| dropper |
| runner |

10. _____

11. _____

12. _____

Phonics Review
Skill: suffix *-er*

Write the word to complete each sentence.

faster   fastest   runner   speaker   winner

1. The _____ ran to the finish line.

2. He ran _____ than his friend.

3. He ran the _____ of all.

4. He was the _____ !

5. The _____ announced the winner.

colder   feeder   highest   longer   loudest

6. That is the _____ bird in the yard.

7. It is singing in the _____ branch.

8. This winter is _____ than last winter.

9. Birds take _____ to find food this year.

10. I like to fill the bird _____ .

Phonics Review
Skill: suffixes -er and -est

Circle the number of syllables for each word.

Name ______________________

1.	snowball	1	2	2.	boxes	1	2
3.	pet	1	2	4.	pens	1	2
5.	funny	1	2	6.	cookbook	1	2

Write the correct word under each picture.

balls dresses peaches trucks

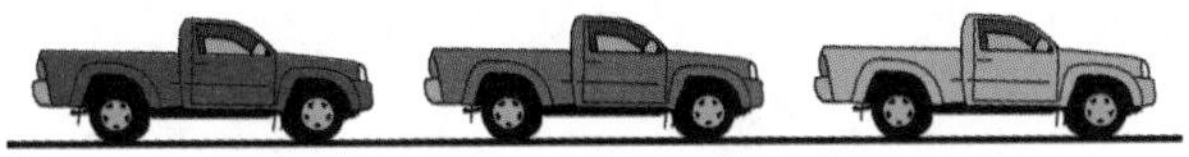

7. ______________________

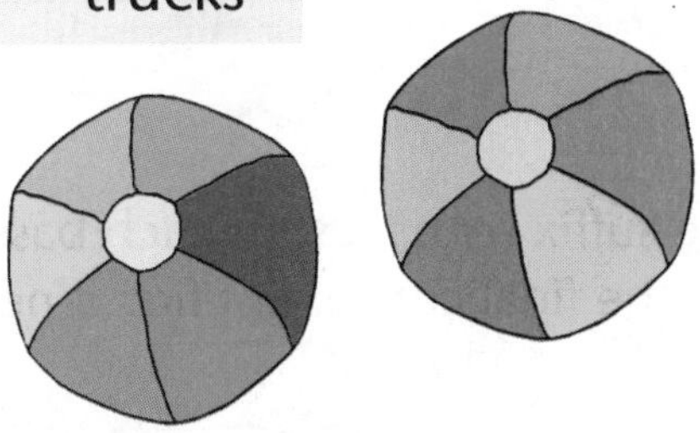

8. ______________________

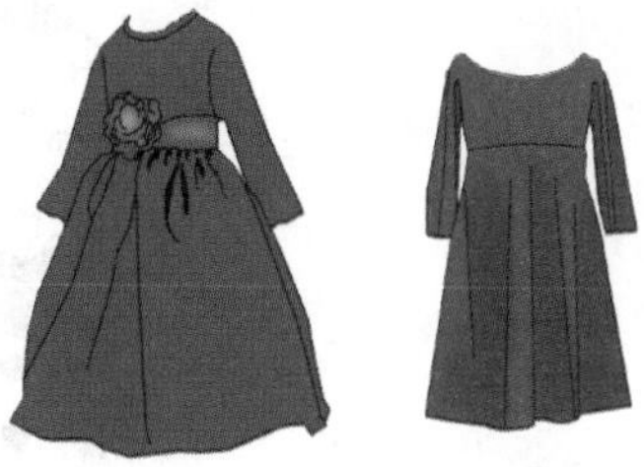

9. ______________________

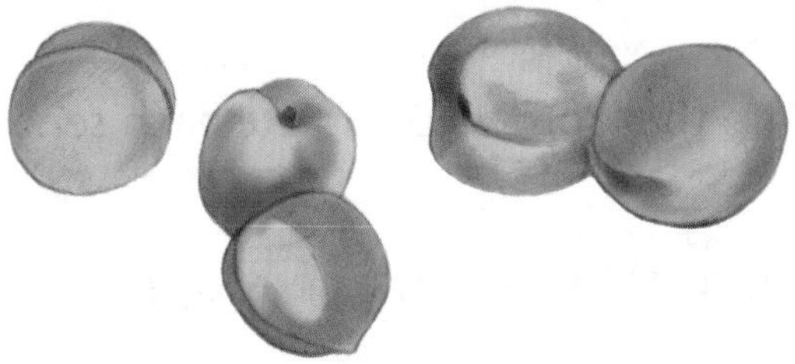

10. ______________________

Underline the base word. Circle the suffix.

11. beds	12. cooked
13. fisher	14. sleeping
15. smallest	16. dishes

Add the suffix *-ing* to each base word.
Double the final consonant first if needed.

1. a splash_____ fish

2. a hop_____ frog

Add the suffix *-ed* to each base word.
Double the final consonant first if needed.

3. a faucet that drip_____

4. a rabbit that jump_____

Add the suffix *-er* or *-est* to each base word.
Double the final consonant first if needed.

5. a run_____ in the race

6. the tall_____ girl in the class

Write the word to complete each sentence.

| biggest | falling | stopped | zipper |

7. The snow was _____ all morning.

8. Mom let us go outside when it _____ .

9. The _____ on my jacket was stuck.

10. We made the _____ snowman on our street.

Phonics Review: *Review*
Skill: short-vowel words with suffixes

Sometimes *y* is changed to *i* before the suffix *-es* or *-ed*. The sound of *y* does not change.
Example: fr*y*, fr*ies*

| butterflies | butterfly | flies |
| fly | spies | spy |

Write the correct word under each picture.

1. _____

2. _____

3. _____

4. _____

5. _____

6. _____

Mark the correct word.

7. Andy ____ to help his mother.

8. He plays with his little sister when she ____.

9. Last night he ____ all the dishes.

10. He set the table while Mother ____ the chicken.

- ⭘ ties   ⭘ tries
- ⭘ cry   ⭘ cries
- ⭘ dried   ⭘ drive
- ⭘ fried   ⭘ fry

Phonics Review
Skill: adding *-ed* or *-es* to words ending in *y*

Draw a line from the word to the correct picture.

1. toys

2. monkeys

3. pennies

4. daisies

5. ladies

Write the plural form of each word by adding *-s* or changing *y* to *i* and adding *-es*.

6. boy   _____

7. baby   _____

8. day   _____

9. city   _____

10. key   _____

Phonics Review
Skill: adding *-es* or *-s* to words ending in *y*

If a word ends in a consonant and *y*, change the *y* to *i* before adding *-er* or *-est*. The sound of *y* does not change.
Example: happy, happier, happiest

Circle the sound *y* makes in each word.

1. sly	ē	ī	2. hungry	ē	ī
3. funny	ē	ī	4. shy	ē	ī

Circle the sound *i* makes when it replaces *y* in each word.

5. sleepier	ē	ī	6. driest	ē	ī
7. angrier	ē	ī	8. flier	ē	ī

Write the base word and add each suffix. Change the *y* to *i* before adding the suffix.

	Add *-er*	**Add *-est***
9. funny	_____	_____
10. happy	_____	_____
11. empty	_____	_____
12. dry	_____	_____

Circle the correct word.

1. I love **stories** / stores about the White House pets.

2. Many of the first **lady** / ladies had dogs.

3. Some of them had **kites** / kitties for pets.

4. The children in the **familys** / families had pets too.

5. The Lincolns had goats and **bunnys** / bunnies .

President George H.W. Bush walks on the White House lawn with Millie and her puppies.

6. Teddy Roosevelt's **boies** / boys took a pony upstairs!

7. President Grant had Shetland **pounces** / ponies for pets.

8. President Harding had **copies** / canaries .

9. He also kept a pen of **turkeys** / turkies .

10. President Bush's dog had **puppies** / poppies at the White House.

Phonics Review
Skill: adding *-es* or *-s* to words ending in *y*

If the first vowel in a word is followed by two consonants and a suffix, the first vowel usually makes its short sound.
Example: licked

If the first vowel in a word is followed by one consonant and a suffix beginning with a vowel, the first vowel usually makes its long sound.
Example: liked

Name _____

Write a macron (ˉ) over the first vowel if it has a long-vowel sound.
Write a breve (˘) over the first vowel if it has a short-vowel sound.

1. liked

2. bumped

3. hitting

4. baked

5. limping

6. raking

7. winning

8. diving

Mark the correct word.

9. Our family was ____ a trip.

10. The box was ____ shut.

11. The frog was ____ into the pond.

12. Emma ____ her leg when she fell.

○ planing   ○ planning

○ taped   ○ tapped

○ hoping   ○ hopping

○ scraped   ○ scrapped

Complete the crossword puzzle using the words in the box.

graded	hiking	racing	saved	shining
smiled	taking	trading	waving	wiped

Across

3. getting from someone
4. made a happy face
6. giving something for something else
8. taking a long walk
9. checked for mistakes

Down

1. moving fast to finish a contest
2. rubbed
4. bright light
5. moving back and forth
7. rescued

Phonics Review
Skill: reading words with *-ed* or *-ing*

When a suffix that begins with a vowel is added to a word that ends in *e*, the *e* is dropped first.
Example: skate, skated, skating

Name

Write the base word and add each suffix.
Drop the *e* before adding the suffix.

	Add *-ing*	**Add** *-ed*
1. wave		
2. bake		
3. bike		
4. time		
5. chase		
6. close		
7. move		
8. grade		
9. joke		
10. name		

Phonics Review
Skill: adding *-ed* or *-ing* to long-vowel words

203

Write the word to complete each sentence. Add the suffix *-ing*.
Some words may need a consonant doubled or an *e* dropped.

bake	lift	scrape	sit	wrap

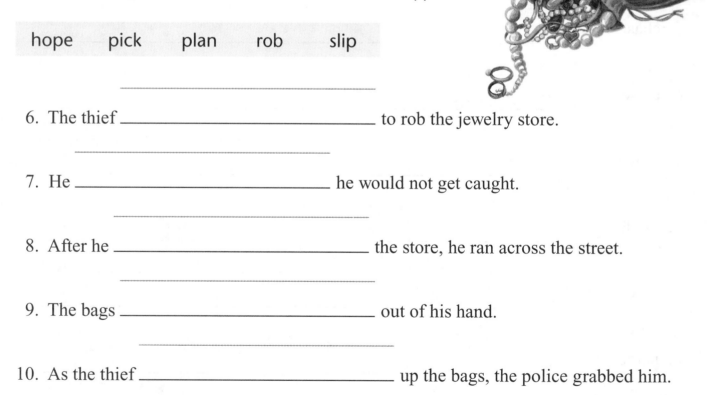

1. Jessie enjoyed _____ cookies.

2. Sam saw her _____ the cookies from the pan.

3. She began _____ the crumbs off the pan.

4. Mom placed the cookies in the gift box _____ on the table.

5. Jessie taped the box shut before _____ it.

Write the word to complete each sentence. Add the suffix *-ed*.
Some words may need a consonant doubled or an *e* dropped.

hope	pick	plan	rob	slip

6. The thief _____ to rob the jewelry store.

7. He _____ he would not get caught.

8. After he _____ the store, he ran across the street.

9. The bags _____ out of his hand.

10. As the thief _____ up the bags, the police grabbed him.

Phonics Review
Skill: adding *-ed* or *-ing* to short- and long-vowel words

When the suffix *-ly* is added to a base word, another syllable is added.
Example: quick, quick(ly) (quick•ly)

Underline the base word. Circle the suffix.

1. s a d l y   2. b o l d l y

Write the word to complete each sentence.

| lightly | neatly | quietly |
| sweetly | swiftly | |

3. Write _____ on the paper.

4. Run _____ to third base.

5. Sit _____ in church.

6. Smile _____ at Mom.

7. Press _____ on the button.

Write the word to complete each phrase.

| bravely | brightly | eagerly |
| loudly | softly | |

8. _____ snored all night

9. _____ opening the gift

10. _____ touched the flower

11. _____ fought the bear

12. _____ shining in the sky

Phonics Review
Skill: suffix *-ly*

205

When the suffix *-ful* is added to a base word, another syllable is added.
Example: play, playful (play•ful)

Write the word that matches each phrase.
Add the suffix *-ful*.

color	fear	harm	help	play

1. likes to have fun

_____

2. is not good for you

_____

3. made with many colors

_____

4. assists someone

_____

5. is afraid

_____

care	cheer	rest	thank	use

6. makes you relax

_____

7. used for some purpose

_____

8. often smiles

_____

9. takes time to think before acting

_____

10. is grateful to God

_____

206

When the suffix *-less* is added to a base word, another syllable is added.
Example: rest, rest(less) (rest•less)

When the suffix *-ness* is added to a base word, another syllable is added.
Example: sad, sad(ness) (sad•ness)

Underline the base word. Circle the suffix.

1. hopeless	2. lateness	3. kindness
4. sadness	5. careless	6. wetness

Write the word to complete each sentence.

brightness	restless
softness	wetness

7. The _____ of the morning sun made us blink.

8. The birds in the trees were _____.

9. We felt the _____ of the breeze as it blew from the south.

10. We felt the _____ of the dew on the grass.

Write the word to complete each sentence.

| biggest | careful | careless | darkness | harmful |

1. Dan was _____ with his bike, and it got rusty.

2. The bike sat in the rain in the _____ .

3. Water is _____ to the paint on a bike.

4. Dan's bike was the _____ bike that he had ever had.

5. Dan will be more _____ the next time he gets a new bike.

| breathless | illness | loudly | singer | speaker |

6. The _____ was going to perform in the afternoon.

7. She had suffered an _____ that had kept her from singing for several weeks.

8. She was introduced by a _____ .

9. When she got up to sing, she felt _____ .

10. The crowd clapped _____ for the famous singer.

Phonics Review
Skill: suffixes

A prefix is added to the beginning of a base word to change the meaning of a word. When the prefix is added, another syllable is added. The prefix *re-* usually means to *do again*. Example: replay

Name _____

Write the word to complete each sentence.

| recall | reenter | reread | rewrite |

1. In a minute, the president will _____ the Oval Office.

2. He will _____ a bill that has been sitting on his desk.

3. The president will ask the senators to _____ the bill.

4. The vice president and president will _____ important matters.

The prefix *a-* can mean *on*. Example: afoot

| aboard | afire | ashore | atop |

5. Sailors climbed _____ the ship.

6. When the sun set, the sky was _____ with brilliant colors.

7. A bird sat high _____ the tree.

8. The sailors went _____ to get food.

The prefixes *un-* and *dis-* make the word mean the opposite.
Examples: unhappy, disagree

unsafe

Mark the correct word.

1. If you eat too much, you may need to ___ your belt.

2. Before you go inside, you will need to ___ the door.

3. The little boy could not get his jacket ___ .

4. It is time to ___ your sleeping bag for the night.

5. ___ the light bulb and put in a new one.

6. We can help Mom ___ the groceries.

○ unbuckle   ○ unbend
○ unpin   ○ unlock
○ unzipped   ○ unlined
○ unsafe   ○ unroll
○ Unscrew   ○ Unseen
○ unpack   ○ unloose

Write the word to complete each sentence.

| disagree | disappear | disconnect |
| disinfect | dislike | dissatisfied |

7. We _____ about who gets to set the table.

8. The clouds may _____ after the sun comes out.

9. The nurse will _____ the counter to kill the germs.

10. We had to _____ the wires when we moved the computer.

11. I _____ having a mess in my room.

12. Dad was _____ with the rusty drill.

210

Pretend that your town has decided to make the biggest pizza, the biggest cake, or some other very large thing. Everyone will read about it in the town newspaper. Use the words in the box or your own words to write about the large thing. Draw a picture of it on the back.

contest	teamwork
working	people
helping	gather
started	supplies
finished	reporter
biggest	voted

THE DAILY NEWS

_____

_____

_____

_____

_____

_____

_____

_____

_____

_____

_____

_____

_____

Phonics Review
Skill: composition

211

Phonics Review
Skill: composition

Our trip to the zoo had ended. We were thankful to God. He showed His goodness in His wonderful creations.

8

A Zoo in the City

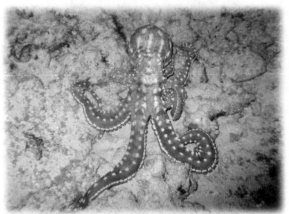

Next we learned about adopting zoo animals. When you adopt an animal, you give money to help support it. Some animals that can be adopted are pandas and flamingos. We told Mom that we wanted to adopt a giant octopus!

6

It was fun to see how the cheetahs chased the lure. It was a flag hooked to a cord. The cheetahs raced around the yard. Their running speed got faster and faster. All families should have as much fun as they did!

3

On our trip to Washington, DC, we stopped at the zoo. We wanted to see the Great Cats Exhibit. The mother cheetah had new cubs.

2

Adopting helps take care of the animals. You help make the exhibits better. You help with medical care. You help buy food for all the zoo animals. We were reminded that God tells us to care for His creatures.

7

Our next stop was the pandas. Parent pandas are bigger than many of the animals at the zoo. But baby pandas are some of the smallest animals.

4

One brave panda cub spent quite a bit of time in the tree. He enjoyed eating his bamboo branches. We gasped loudly when we were told that a panda can eat forty pounds of bamboo in a day.

5

Add the suffix -s or -es to each word to show
more than one item.

Name

1. glass_____

2. pen_____

3. brush_____

Write the base word and add the suffix -ed.
The words may need a consonant doubled or an e dropped.

4. pave   _____

5. bat   _____

6. time   _____

Write the base word and add the suffix -ing.
The words may need a consonant doubled or an e dropped.

7. skate _____

8. pot   _____

9. grade _____

Write the base word and add the suffix -es.
Change the y to i before adding the suffix.

10. pony _____

11. city _____

12. copy _____

© 2007 BJU Press. Reproduction prohibited.

Circle the number of syllables for each word.

1. beaches	1	2		2. kicks	1	2
3. blended	1	2		4. slowest	1	2
5. filled	1	2		6. cupcake	1	2

Add the prefix *un-, dis-, a-,* or *re-* to make a new word.
Use each prefix once.

7. _____agree

8. _____play

9. _____happy

10. _____float

bigger	colorful	gentleness
hottest	illness	slowly

Write the word to complete each sentence.

11. Shawn made a _____ painting with many bright colors.

12. We like our vet because of his _____ with the animals.

13. A serious _____ kept Alex out of school for several weeks.

14. That snowman is _____ than the one we made last year.

15. This is the _____ chili I have ever eaten!

16. Jon was so tired that he woke up very _____ this morning.

216

Unit 6

Space

Eileen M. Berry

Outer space and inner space
And space between the stars—
Too much space to measure
In this universe of ours.

Space to hold the galaxies,
The planets, moons, and suns,
Comets, constellations,
Stars that weigh a billion tons!

Space for holes so vast and black
They swallow all the light;
Meteors careening
In their headlong, hurried flight.

What a place of mystery
And glorious design!
Heaven's darkened backdrop
Where God's handiwork can shine.

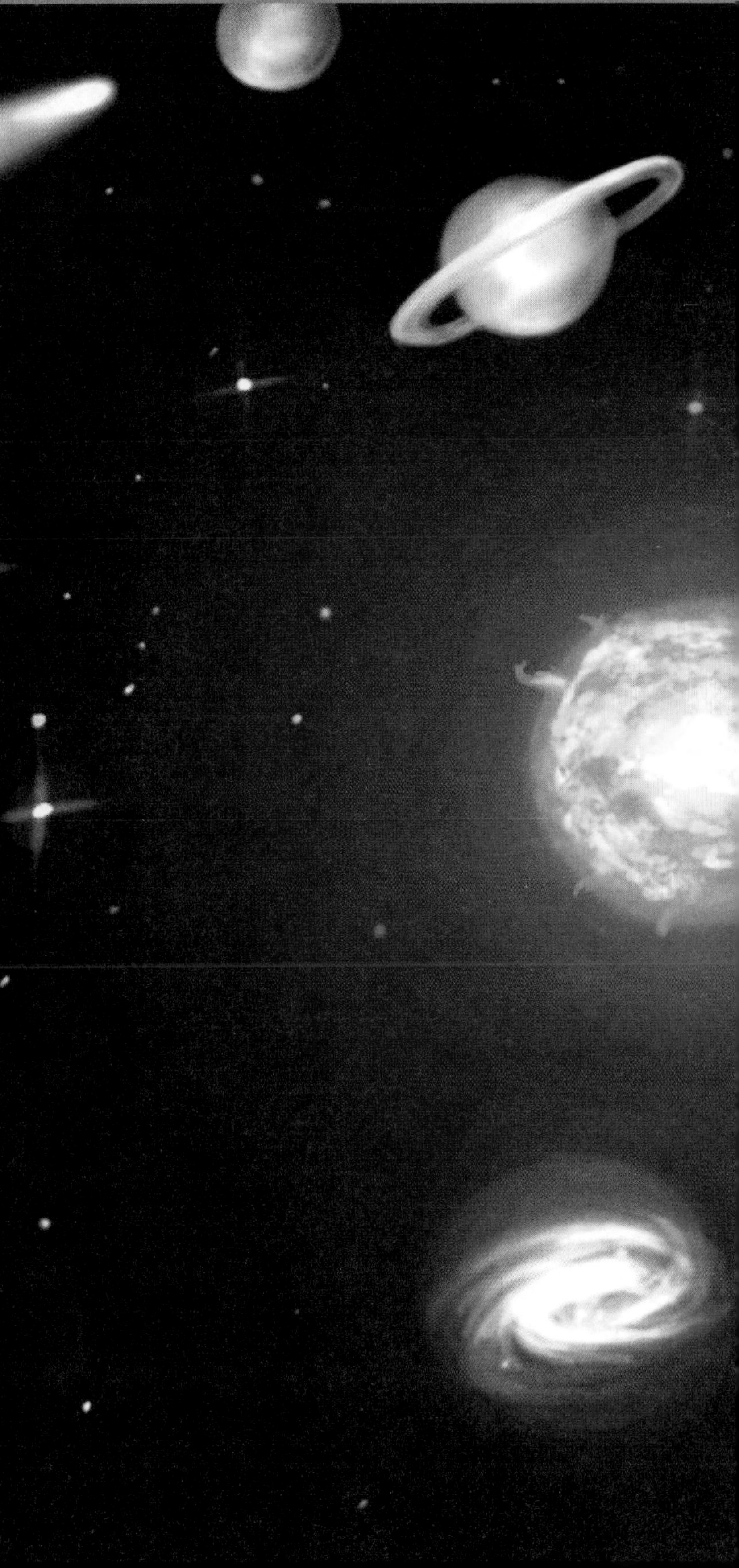

Unit 6 Contents

Wr 219

Wr, mb 220

Kn, lf, lk 221

Silent Consonants 222

Words with *dge* and *ge* 223

Words with *ch* and *tch* 224

Ph as /f/ 225

Consonant Digraphs 226

Short Vowels 227–28

Long Vowels 229–30

Special Vowel Sounds 231–32

Ea as /ĕ/ 233

Ea as /ĕ/ and /ē/ 234

Special Word Families 235–36

Homophones 237

Synonyms 238

Antonyms 239

Antonyms, Synonyms, and Homophones 240

Contractions 241–42

Composition 243–44

Reading a Story 245–46

Checkup 247–48

The consonant pair *wr* usually says /r/.
The *w* is silent.
Example: wrote

Name _____

Write the letter of the correct phrase in the blank.

_____ 1. wren   a. a tool

_____ 2. wrong   b. a bird

_____ 3. write   c. not correct

_____ 4. wrench   d. to put letters on paper

_____ 5. wrap   a. a circle of leaves, flowers, or branches

_____ 6. wrist   b. to cover

_____ 7. wreath   c. a truck that removes smashed cars

_____ 8. wrecker   d. a body part

_____ 9. wrinkle   a. to twist and squeeze

_____ 10. wring   b. a small crease or fold

_____ 11. wreck   c. to ruin or destroy

_____ 12. wrath   d. great anger

Phonics Review
Skill: *wr* as /r/

Write the word to complete each sentence.

climb   crumbs   limb   wrens   Wright

1. The birds sat on the _____ of the tree.

2. My dad told me that the birds are called _____.

3. Mom gave us some bread _____ to give the birds to eat.

4. Mr. _____ taught us about birds in science class.

5. I saw a squirrel _____ past the nest.

numb   thumb   wrecked   wrench   wrong

6. Dad asked me to help him fix the _____ car.

7. He had me hand him a _____.

8. It was so cold outside my hands felt _____.

9. We went back to the store because we bought the _____ headlight.

10. I yelped when I smashed my _____.

Phonics Review
Skill: *wr* as /r/ and *mb* as /m/

The consonant pair *kn* usually says /n/.
The *k* is silent.
Example: knee

The consonant pair *lk* usually says /k/.
The *l* is silent.
Example: chalk

The consonant pair *lf* usually says /f/.
The *l* is silent.
Example: half

Draw a line from the phrase to the correct picture.
Each picture will match two phrases.

1. kneeling to the king

3. a tight knot

2. a knit scarf

4. a brave knight

5. a knock on a door

7. a shiny knob

6. a sharp knife

8. kneading bread

9. half an orange

11. a little calf

10. a stalk of corn

12. talk to Dad

Help the rocket get to the moon. Trace the path, going through the words that have a silent consonant. Write the words with a silent consonant under the correct heading.

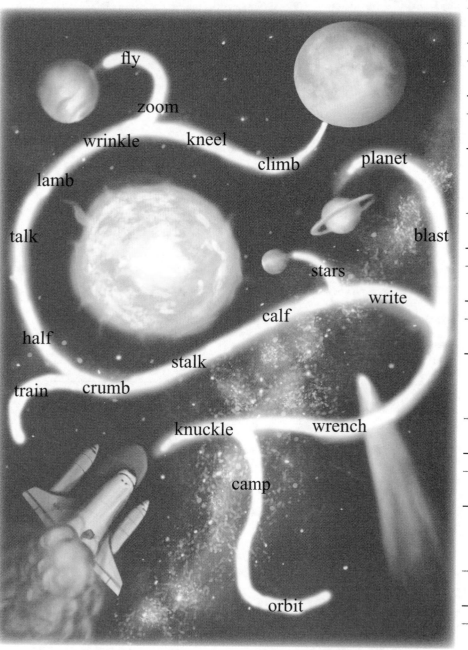

wr

_____

_____

_____

_____

_____

mb

_____

_____

_____

_____

kn

_____

_____

_____

lk

_____

_____

_____

lf

_____

_____

_____

Phonics Review
Skill: silent letters

The letters *dge* and *ge* usually say /j/.
The vowel is usually short before *dge*.
The *d* is silent.
Example: edge

The vowel is usually long before *ge*.
Example: age

Name _____

cage
page
stage

badge
Madge

Write the correct word under each picture.
(Not all words will be used.)

edge
hedge
pledge

bridge
ridge

dodge
lodge

1. _____

2. _____

3. _____

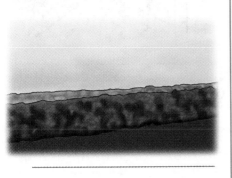

4. _____

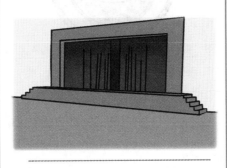

5. _____

6. _____

Write a macron (ˉ) over the first vowel if it has a long-vowel sound.
Write a breve (˘) over the first vowel if it has a short-vowel sound.

7. p l e d g e

8. n u d g e

9. r a g e

10. a g e

11. e d g e

12. h u g e

Phonics Review
Skill: words with *dge* and *ge*

Write the correct word under each picture.

beach	crutch	latch	match	patch	peach

1. _____

2. _____

3. _____

4. _____

5. _____

6. _____

Circle the correct word.

7. Fetch / Match the bone.

8. Etch / Pitch the ball.

9. Match / Itch the socks.

10. Scratch / Latch the gate.

Write a macron (‾) over the first vowel if it has a long-vowel sound.
Write a breve (˘) over the first vowel if it has a short-vowel sound.

11. s k e t c h

12. h u t c h

13. r e a c h

224

A consonant digraph is formed when two consonants together make one sound.
Examples: chase, whale, phone

Name

Write the correct word under each picture.

chicken	elephant	fish	graph	phone
photograph	saxophone	toothbrush	trophy	wheat

1. _____

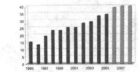

2. _____

3. _____

4. _____

5. _____

6. _____

7. _____

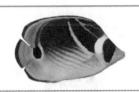

8. _____

9. _____

10. _____

Phonics Review
Skill: *ph* as /f/; consonant digraph review

Mark the correct sentence.

1.

  ○ The elephant is spraying water into the air.

  ○ Beth learned how to read by using phonics.

2.

  ○ The team won a huge trophy for soccer.

  ○ Please answer the telephone.

3.

  ○ Grandma has an old photograph of her family.

  ○ Chad has a photo of the sailboat.

4.

  ○ Shawn can say the alphabet backwards!

  ○ My nephew loves to skate.

5.

  ○ I can say some phrases in Spanish.

  ○ That child is throwing a ball.

6.

  ○ The funny clown juggled three balls.

  ○ This photo is too dark.

Phonics Review
Skill: consonant digraphs

Draw a picture to illustrate each underlined word.   Name _____

1. I tipped my <u>glass</u>, spilled some <u>milk</u>, and got the <u>mop</u> to clean it up.

2. Jed slept on the <u>cot</u>, I slept on the top <u>bunk</u>, and Max rested on the <u>rug</u>.

3. My <u>cat</u> sat on the <u>mat</u> and slept in the <u>sun</u>.

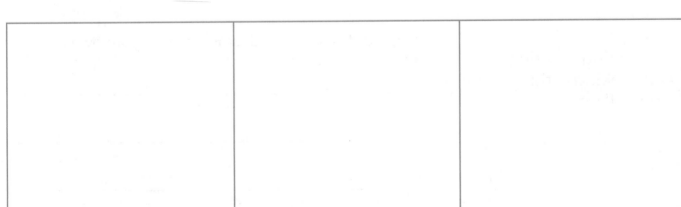

Phonics Review
Skill: short vowels

Choose words from the word families to write one,
two, or three lines that rhyme with the first line.

sack	pack	back
tack	jack	lack
Mack	black	

Jim got out his sack
When it was time to pack.
His sack was green and black.
He put it on his back.

tick	stick	lick
sick	kick	wick
pick	Rick	

My dog can fetch a stick

_____

_____
_____

_____
_____

_____ .

jet	vet	pet
wet	let	yet
met	set	

Grandma flew on a jet

_____

_____
_____

_____
_____

_____ .

sing	ring	bring
king	wing	thing
zing	fling	

Choose words from the word family to write your own rhyme.

_____

_____
_____

_____
_____

_____ .

Phonics Review
Skill: short vowels

Circle the correct word.

1. Joe has **five / hive** pairs of shoes.

2. He put on his tennis shoes and went to pick up the **jail / mail** .

3. He changed to his dress shoes when he wore his **fruit / suit** .

4. He joined the **seam / team** at an awards dinner.

5. Joe **tore / wore** his slippers at home to keep his feet warm.

6. Do you think **hoe / Joe** likes to wear his flip-flops in the summer?

7. Joe wore his work boots to **doe / hoe** the weeds in the garden.

8. His work paid off when he gathered the **fruit / suit** .

9. Joe's **dream / seam** is to own some cowboy boots.

10. Joe would like to have **more / tore** shoes.

Write the words to complete the story.

day	gray	rain
rainbow	shore	so

At the Beach

_____

We went to the _____ last summer. We had

_____ _____

_____ much fun. One _____

_____

it rained, and we saw a pretty _____. We found

_____

lots of _____ and pink shells in the sand after the

_____

_____.

beach	bikes	boat	night
seagulls	time	week	

_____

We played with a _____ ball

_____

and rode our _____ along the shore.

_____

The _____ swooped down and ate bread on

_____

the deck. One _____ we went out on a fishing

_____ _____

_____. The _____

_____

passed quickly and soon it was _____ to leave.

230

Write the phrases to complete the story.

dog's bark	flower garden	green ferns
little park	long strides	red bird
small turtle	thick cord	tiny girl
wild turkey		

At the Park

_____ _____ _____

A _____ _____ flew over the _____

_____ _____ _____

_____ . A _____ _____

_____

made its way slowly across the path. The sound of a _____

_____ _____

_____ came from the trees. A _____

_____ _____

_____ flew up from the _____

_____ _____

_____ . The _____ _____ was

_____ _____

beginning to fill with people. A _____ _____ picked

up some fallen rose petals and tucked them in her purse.

_____ _____

A _____ _____ kept

her away from the other flowers.

_____

A runner burst into _____

_____

_____ as he went down the hill.

Phonics Review
Skill: special vowel sounds

Complete the crossword puzzle using the words in the box.

| chirp | crawl | fall | | germs | horse | launch | orbit |
| point | purse | shooting | | sound | star | toss | toys |

Across

2. a bright light in the night sky
3. to send off
6. the sharp end of a pin
7. what planets do when they go around the sun
10. you play with them
11. they can make you sick
12. you can hear it

Down

1. come down
2. moving quickly
4. the sound a bird makes
5. throw
6. Mom carries things in it
8. animal that can pull a cart
9. what a baby does to move

Phonics Review
Skill: special vowel sounds

Write the correct word under each picture.

| arrowhead | bedspread | bread | breakfast | feathers |
| head | headlight | leather | thread | wealth |

1. _____

2. _____

3. _____

4. _____

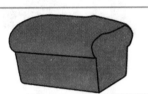

5. _____

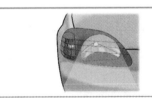

6. _____

7. _____

8. _____

9. _____

10. _____

Write each word in the correct column.

Short _e_

Long _e_

Phonics Review
Skill: _ea_ as /ĕ/ in _bread_ and _ea_ as /ē/ in _leaf_

Draw a line from the phrase to the correct picture.

1. a baby cries

2. a foot of snow

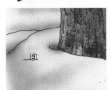

3. a king's crown

4. a piece of wood

5. a yield sign

6. a horn to blow

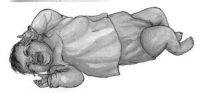

7. my helpful niece

8. a sturdy shield

9. an apple pie

10. a funny clown

Phonics Review
Skill: special word families

Write the word to complete each sentence. *(Not all words will be used.)*

cold	bolt	bind	child
hold	colt	find	mild
mold	jolt	mind	wild
old		wind	
sold			
told			

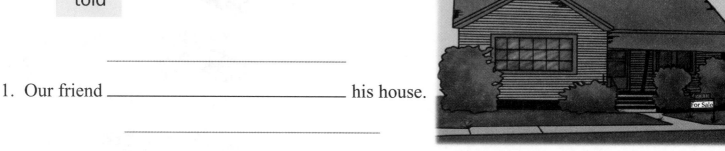

1. Our friend _____ his house.

2. A pipe in the _____ house was sagging.

3. Our friend _____ Dad he'd pay him to fix it.

4. We went down to the _____ basement.

5. We had to _____ the pipe and fix it.

6. Dad had to replace a _____ near the pipes.

7. The new bolt would _____ up the pipe.

8. Dad saw some _____ in the basement too.

9. Dad didn't _____ getting rid of the mold at the same time.

10. It was just a _____ problem, so he scrubbed it with bleach.

236

Phonics Review
Skill: special word families

Homophones are words that sound alike but have different spellings and different meanings.
Example: hear, here

Name _____

Draw a line to match the homophones.

1. see   cent

2. sent   sea

3. weak   week

4. sale   sail

5. pail   tail

6. tale   pale

7. road   heel

8. heal   rode

9. due   stare

10. stair   there

11. their   roll

12. role   dew

13. rose   deer

14. break   meet

15. meat   brake

16. dear   rows

Mark the correct synonym.

 1. big   ○ little   ○ large   ○ round

 2. sick   ○ tired   ○ need   ○ ill

 3. wet   ○ dry   ○ damp   ○ hard

4. quick   ○ fast   ○ slow   ○ jump

 5. small   ○ big   ○ long   ○ little

 6. junk   ○ trash   ○ treasure   ○ collection

  7. noise   ○ whisper   ○ sound   ○ touch

 8. shut   ○ close   ○ open   ○ carry

 9. stole   ○ sold   ○ placed   ○ took

 10. sleep   ○ work   ○ run   ○ nap

  11. enjoy   ○ like   ○ take   ○ need

12. bugs   ○ dogs   ○ insects   ○ kittens

238

Phonics Review
Skill: synonyms

Name _____

Mark the correct antonym.

1. small   ○ little   ○ large   ○ tiny

2. rough   ○ bumpy   ○ rugged   ○ smooth

3. slow   ○ fast   ○ soft   ○ pokey

4. grouchy   ○ mean   ○ sad   ○ happy

5. walk   ○ stroll   ○ skip   ○ sit

6. over   ○ under   ○ beside   ○ above

7. hard   ○ difficult   ○ easy   ○ bumpy

8. found   ○ lost   ○ take   ○ pound

9. early   ○ timely   ○ slow   ○ late

10. hot   ○ cold   ○ warm   ○ bright

11. right   ○ west   ○ left   ○ east

12. clean   ○ dirty   ○ sharp   ○ polished

astronaut: a space explorer

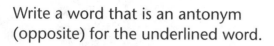

Write a word that is an antonym
(opposite) for the underlined word.

1. An astronaut puts <u>on</u> his suit before going out of the spaceship. _____

2. His suit is <u>thick</u> to protect him from hot or cold air. _____

3. The chest piece is <u>hard</u> to protect him. _____

4. He makes sure his air tank is <u>full</u>. _____

Underline the word that is a synonym for the word in the box.

speak	5. While walking in space, astronauts use radios to talk to each other.
labor	6. They lock their boots in brackets so they will not float as they work.
grasping	7. They walk around holding tightly to handles.
little	8. They use small rockets to move away from the shuttle.

Mark the correct homophone. Use the dictionary if you need help.

9. The astronauts can ___ the earth far away.   ○ see   ○ sea

10. From space, it looks like a tiny ___.   ○ bawl   ○ ball

11. The astronauts have an important ___ in telling us about space.   ○ role   ○ roll

12. ___ suits are fitted with small cameras.   ○ Their   ○ There

Phonics Review
Skills: antonyms; synonyms; homophones

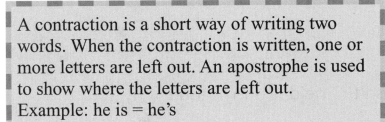

A contraction is a short way of writing two words. When the contraction is written, one or more letters are left out. An apostrophe is used to show where the letters are left out.
Example: he is = he's

Name _____

Draw a line from the word pair to the correct contraction.

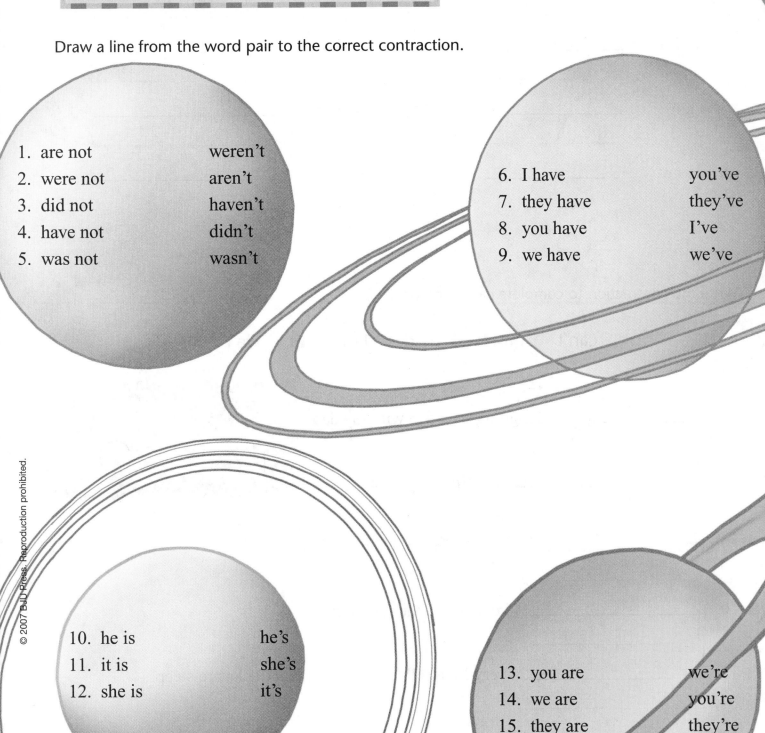

1. are not   weren't
2. were not   aren't
3. did not   haven't
4. have not   didn't
5. was not   wasn't

6. I have   you've
7. they have   they've
8. you have   I've
9. we have   we've

10. he is   he's
11. it is   she's
12. she is   it's

13. you are   we're
14. we are   you're
15. they are   they're

Phonics Review
Skill: contractions

Write the contraction for each word pair.

| can't | don't | hasn't | he'd | I'm | isn't |

1. he would _____

2. has not _____

3. I am _____

4. cannot _____

5. do not _____

6. is not _____

Write the contraction to complete each sentence.

| can't | hasn't | he'd | I'm | it's | we're |

7. _____ going on a trip with my dad.

8. I _____ wait till we get there.

9. He _____ taken me to this place before.

10. _____ like to go on the fastest ride.

11. _____ a very long roller coaster, and its tracks are steep.

12. _____ going to have so much fun!

Phonics Review
Skill: contractions

Imagine that you are taking a trip to space. What would you take? What would it be like inside your rocket? Would people at home know about your trip? Use the words in the box or your own words to write about your trip to space.

On the back, draw a picture of something you might see as you fly through space.

Name _____

space	planets	stars	moon	night
bright	rocket	spacesuit	food	tank
float	telescope	signal	talk	made
plans	know	rocks	wrong	alone

_____

_____

_____

_____

_____

_____

_____

_____

_____

_____

_____

_____

_____

Phonics Review
Skill: composition

244

Phonics Review
Skill: composition

Betsy read that no person has ever counted all the stars. There are too many. But God has counted and named all the things in space. What an amazing God!

8

Space

1

Betsy knows that God made all the things she can see and not see in space. She read in the Bible that God made the sun, moon, and stars on the fourth day of Creation.

6

When she was little, her mother helped her learn "Twinkle, Twinkle, Little Star." She liked to see the stars twinkle. Now she knows that they seem to sparkle because of thick layers of moving air.

3

Betsy loves to sit on the porch and look up at the stars. She likes to read books about space. There are photos of planets and stars. She reads about places she can't see.

2

Betsy learned that the world is part of the Milky Way. That made her think of a candy bar when she first heard the name. Now she knows it is a group of billions of stars and planets. The sun is one of the stars in the Milky Way.

7

Some nights her dad comes outside with her. He loves to point out stars in the sky. One that he likes to find is the North Star.

4

Dad started with the Big Dipper. It looks like a cup with a long handle. Two stars in that patch of the sky point to the North Star. He said that if you found that star, it would help you find your way at night.

5

Draw a line to match the synonyms.

Name _____

1. bug   damp

2. chore   fast

3. wet   work

4. quick   insect

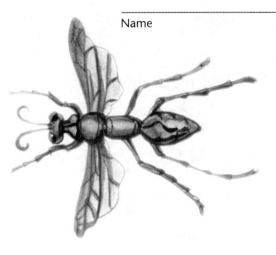

Write the contraction for each word pair.

_____

5. do not _____

_____

6. I am _____

_____

7. is not _____

_____

8. he is _____

Mark the correct antonyms (opposites).

9. right   ⭕ wrong   ⭕ bright   10. lost   ⭕ found   ⭕ fast

11. quick   ⭕ quiet   ⭕ slow   12. end   ⭕ stand   ⭕ start

Mark the correct homophone.

13. The puppy wagged his ___.   ⭕ tail   ⭕ tale

14. He ate from his ___ bowl.   ⭕ blue   ⭕ blew

15. Then he ran down the ___ to play in the yard. ⭕ stares   ⭕ stairs

Write a macron (‾) over the first vowel if it has a long-vowel sound.
Write a breve (˘) over the first vowel if it has a short-vowel sound.

16. lamp   17. space   18. flight   19. suit   20. flung

21. fleet   22. hole   23. mend   24. spin   25. shot

Phonics Review: Checkup
Skills: synonyms; contractions; antonyms; homophones; long and short vowels

247

Mark the correct word.

1. The _____ came to take the car away.   ○ wreck   ○ wrecker

2. I hurt my _____.   ○ knob   ○ knee

3. Dwight is going to take his _____ to the vet.   ○ calf   ○ half

4. The shepherd led the _____ to the still water.   ○ lambs   ○ lamps

5. The teacher let us use the _____.   ○ talk   ○ chalk

Use the key to color the balls.

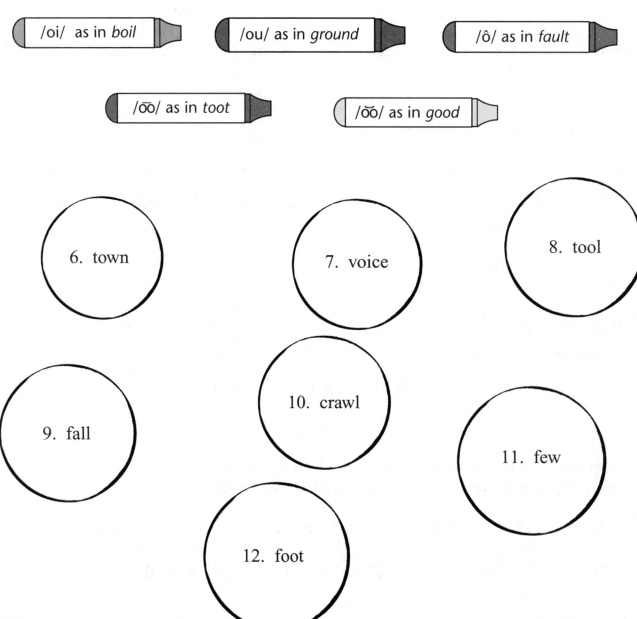

/oi/ as in *boil*

/ou/ as in *ground*

/ô/ as in *fault*

/o͞o/ as in *toot*

/o͝o/ as in *good*

6. town

7. voice

8. tool

9. fall

10. crawl

11. few

12. foot

Phonics Review: *Checkup*
Skills: consonant digraphs; special vowel sounds

Rules and Definitions

Consonants

◆ A consonant blend is formed when two or three consonant sounds are said together quickly.

Examples: sled, trick, drop, skip, splinter, strong, jump, rust, sand

◆ A consonant digraph is formed when two consonants together make one sound.

Sometimes two consonants make the same sound.

Examples: cuff, miss, buzz, butter, haystack, locket

Sometimes the two consonants make one new sound that is different from both of the regular sounds.

Examples: shot, chin, thank, phone

Sometimes one of the consonants in the pair is silent.

Examples: wrote, crumb, knee, chalk, half

◆ *C* usually says /k/ when it is followed by another consonant.

Examples: clock, cycle

C usually says /k/ when it is followed by *a, o,* or *u.* This *c* is called a *hard c.*

Examples: cave, coat, cup

C usually says /s/ when it is followed by *e, i,* or *y.* This *c* is called a *soft c.*

Examples: cent, circus, cycle

◆ The letters *tch* usually say /ch/. The *t* is silent, so only the digraph *ch* is heard.

Example: itch

◆ *G* usually says /g/ when it is followed by another consonant or is at the end of a word.

Examples: great, bug

G usually says /g/ when it is followed by *a, o,* or *u.* This *g* is called a *hard g.*

Examples: gate, go, gust

G usually says /j/ when it is followed by *e, i,* or *y.* This *g* is called a *soft g.*

Examples: gentle, giraffe, gym

◆ The letters *dge* usually say /j/. The *d* is silent. The vowel is usually short before *dge.*

Example: edge

249

Vowels

The **vowels** are *a, e, i, o, u,* and sometimes *y.* They each say more than one sound.

Short Vowels

♦ When a word or syllable has one vowel followed by one or more consonants, the vowel usually says its short sound.

Short *a* says /ă/ as in *bag* and *tack.*
Short *e* says /ĕ/ as in *pet* and *rest.*
Short *i* says /ĭ/ as in *dip* and *fish.*
Short *o* says /ŏ/ as in *mom* and *rock.*
Short *u* says /ŭ/ as in *cup* and *spun.*
Short *y* says /ĭ/ as in *gym* and *Lynn.*

♦ When a vowel is followed by two consonants and *-le*, it has a short vowel sound.

The *-le* at the end of a word says /əl/.

Examples: giggle, crackle, twinkle

♦ The vowel pair *ea* sometimes says the short *e* sound.

Example: spread

♦ A breve ˘ may be written over a vowel to show that it makes its short sound.

Example: băt

Long Vowels

♦ When a vowel says its long sound, it usually says its own name.

Long *a* says /ā/ as in *sail.*
Long *e* says /ē/ as in *feet.*
Long *i* says /ī/ as in *smile.*
Long *o* says /ō/ as in *boat.*
Long *u* says /ū/(/yoo/) as in *mule* or /oo/ as in *rule.*
Long *y* says /ī/ as in *by* or /ē/ as in *bunny.*

♦ When one vowel is followed by one consonant and a final *e*, the first vowel is long and the *e* is silent.

Examples: cake, Steve, hide, drove, cute

♦ When two vowels are together, they may be called a vowel pair.

Often in a vowel pair (digraph), the first vowel is long and the second one is silent.

Examples: trail, pray, seal, seeds, pie, coal, flown, true, fruit

♦ The letter *w* sometimes acts as the silent second vowel in a vowel pair. The vowel pair *ow* may say the long *o* sound.

Examples: grow, blown

♦ When there is one vowel at the end of a word or syllable, it often says its long sound.

Examples: we, go

250

- When the first vowel is followed by one consonant and -le, the vowel is usually long.

  Examples: noble, maple

- The letter y is a consonant at the beginning of a syllable, but in other positions, it may act as a vowel.

  When y follows an a, the y may act as the silent second vowel in a vowel pair. The vowel pair ay says the long a sound.

  Examples: day, play

  The letter y acts like a vowel at the end of a word or syllable.

  When y is the only vowel at the end of a one-syllable word, it usually says /ī/.

  Examples: fly, dry

  When y is the only vowel at the end of a word with more than one syllable, it usually says /ē/.

  Examples: happy, funny

- Some word families do not follow the rules. A few word families have one vowel with a long vowel sound.

  Examples: old, grind, child, colt, roll

- Sometimes the long i sound is spelled igh. The letters gh are silent.

  Examples: sigh, light

- The vowel pair ie sometimes says /ē/.

  Examples: thief, niece, shriek, yield

- A macron ‾ may be written over a vowel to show that it makes its long sound.

  Example: bāit

Special Vowel Patterns

- Sometimes a vowel pair makes one sound that is different from either of the two vowels.

  The vowel pair oo sometimes says its long sound, /o͞o/.

  Example: zoo

  The vowel pair oo sometimes says its short sound, /o͝o/.

  Example: book

  The vowel pair ew may say /o͞o/ or /yo͞o/.

  Examples: new, few

  The vowel pairs oi and oy may say /oi/.

  Examples: oil, boy

  The vowel pairs au and aw may say /ô/.

  Examples: faucet, draw

  The vowel pairs ou and ow may say /ou/.

  Examples: mouse, towel

- When r follows a vowel, it influences the vowel's sound.

  Usually or says /ôr/ as in horn.
  Usually ar says /är/ as in barn.
  Usually er, ir, and ur say /ûr/ as in her, bird, and nurse.

- When o is followed by ss, st, th, or ft, it may say /ô/.

  Examples: loss, lost, moth, soft

- When a is followed by two ls, it usually says /ô/.

  Example: fall

Base Words, Prefixes, Suffixes, and Syllables

- A base word is a word to which something is added that will change the word.

  Example: thank, thanks, thanking, unthankful

- A prefix is added to the beginning of a base word to change the meaning of a word.

  The prefix *re-* usually means to *do again*.

  Example: replay

  The prefix *a-* can mean *on*.

  Example: afoot

  The prefixes *un-* and *dis-* make the word mean the opposite.

  Examples: unhappy, disagree

- A suffix is an ending that is added to a base word to change the use of the word.

  Example: camp, camps, camped, camping

- The suffix *-s* is added to many nouns to show more than one. Nouns that show more than one are plural.

  Example: ball, balls

  The suffix *-es* is added to nouns that end in *x*, *ss*, *sh*, or *ch* to make them plural.

  Example: glass, glasses

- The suffix *-s* or *-es* is added to a verb to change the word. The noun and verb must fit together.

  Examples:
  Many lions *roar*, but one lion *roars*.
  Many men *preach*, but one man *preaches*.

- The suffix *-ing* may be added to a base word to change the tense.

  Example: jump, jumping (jump•ing)

- The suffix *-ed* may be added to a base word to change the tense. The suffix *-ed* makes the sound of /t/ as in *pitched*, /d/ as in *played*, or /ed/ as in *waited (wait•ed)*.

- The suffix *-er* may be added to a base word to compare two things.

  The suffix *-est* may be added to compare more than two things.

  Example: short, shorter, shortest

- The suffix *-er* may be added to some action verbs to change them to nouns.

  Example: catch, catcher

- If the first vowel in a word is followed by two consonants and a suffix, the first vowel usually makes its short sound.

  Example: lick + ed → licked

- If the first vowel in a word is followed by one consonant and a suffix beginning with a vowel, the first vowel usually makes its long sound.

  Example: like + ed → liked

- When a short-vowel word ends in a single consonant, usually the consonant is doubled before adding a suffix that begins with a vowel.

  Example: clap, claps, clapped, clapping, clapper

- When a suffix that begins with a vowel is added to a word that ends in *e*, the *e* is dropped first.

  Example: skate, skated, skating

- If a word ends in a vowel and *y*, the *y* does not change when *-s* is added.

  Example: turkey, turkeys

- If a word ends in a consonant and *y*, change the *y* to *i* before adding *-es*, *-ed, -er,* or *-est*. The sound of *y* does not change.

  Examples: happy, happier, happiest; puppy, puppies; dry, dried

- Words have one or more parts or syllables. Each syllable has one vowel sound.

  Sun has one vowel sound, /ŭ/, so it has one syllable.

  Sunshine has two vowel sounds, /ŭ/ and /ī/, so it has two syllables.

- Many times when a prefix or suffix is added to a word, another syllable is added.

  Examples: a•sleep, re•turn, patch•es, jump•ing, wait•ed, quick•ly, play•ful, sad•ness, rest•less

- When the suffix *-s* is added to a word, the number of syllables does not change.

  Example: crow, crows

Definitions

- A word family has rhyming words with the same spelling at the end.

  Example: in, bin, fin, tin, spin, shin

- Homophones are words that sound alike but have different spellings and different meanings.

  Examples: hear, here; hew, hue

- Synonyms are words that have almost the same meaning.

  Example: rock, stone

- Antonyms are words that are opposite in meaning.

  Example: stop, go

- A contraction is a short way of writing two words. When the contraction is written, one or more letters are left out. An apostrophe is used to show where the letters are left out.

  Example: he is = he's

- A compound word is formed when two words are combined to make a new word.

  Examples: goldfish, lunchbox

254

Index

Antonyms, 239–40
Checkups, 39–40, 67–68, 131–32, 169–70, 215–16, 247–48
Composition, 63, 127, 165, 211–12, 243–44
Compound words, 123–24
Consonants
    beginning sounds, 3–4, 7–8
    consonant blends, 29–30
        beginning, 19–21
        beginning three-letter, 18, 22
        blends and digraphs, 37–38
        ending, 25–28
        l blends, 13–14
        r blends, 15–16
        s blends, 17–18
    consonant digraphs, 34–36
        beginning, *ch, sh, th, wh*, 31–32
        ck, 12
        ending, *ch, sh, th*, 33
        ph as /f/, 225–26
    ending sounds, 5–8, 11
    hard and soft *c*, 115–16, 119–20
    hard and soft *g*, 117–20
    middle, 9–11
    silent consonants
        ch and *tch*, 224
        dge and *ge*, 223
        lf, lk, kn, 221
        review, 222
        wr, mb, 219–20
Contractions, 241–42
Homophones, 141, 237, 240
Poems
    "At the Canyon Rim," 133
    "At the Zoo," 69
    "The Park Is the Place," 41
    "Space," 217
    "To Grandma's House," 1
    "Washington, DC," 171
Prefixes
    re-, a-, un-, dis-, 209–10
Reading a story, 65–66, 129–30, 167–68, 213–14, 245–46
Review, 23–24, 53–54, 103–4, 151–52, 166, 195–96
Rhyming words, 55–56
Suffixes, 208
    after silent *e*, 201–4
    changing *y* to *i* before suffixes, 197–200
    -ed and *-ing* to a base word, 181–82, 185–86, 197
    -ed and *-ing* to long-vowel words, 203–4
    -ed to short-vowel words, 187–88, 190, 201–2
    -er and *-est*, 191–94, 199
    -ful, 206
    -ing to short-vowel words, 187, 189–90, 201–2, 204
    -less, -ness, 207
    -ly, 205
    -s or *-es*, 175–81, 197–98, 200
    sounds of the suffix *-ed*, 183–84

Syllables, 173–74
Synonyms, 238, 240
Vowels
    long, 98, 102, 126, 128, 229–30
        a, 71, 75–76, 83, 90
        a and *e*, 84
        a digraph *ai*, 73
        a digraph *ay*, 74
        a VCe, 72
        e, 77, 80–83, 90, 122
        e digraphs *ea, ee*, 78, 234
        e open syllables, 79
        e spelled *ie*, 121, 235
        i, 85, 89–90, 122
        i as *igh*, 87
        in closed syllables, 113–14, 236
        in open syllables, 94
        i VCe, 86
        -le after long vowels, 105–6
        macron, 76, 82, 96, 106
        o, 91, 95–96
        o digraphs *oa, ow*, 93
        o VCe, 92
        rhymes, 97
        spelling, 125
        u, 99–101
        y as long *e*, 109–12
        y as long *i*, 107–8, 111–12
    short, 64, 98, 227–28
        a, 43–44, 76, 83, 90
        and *-le*, 57–59, 106
        breve, 76, 82, 96, 106
        e, 45–46, 82–83, 90
        i, 47–48, 88, 90
        o, 49–50, 96
        spelling words, 60–62
        u, 51–52, 101
    special vowels
        all sound, 154
        au and *aw*, 155–56
        ea as /ĕ/, 233–34
        ew sound, 141–42
        long and short *oo*, 139–40
        long-vowel digraph /o͞o/, 135–36, 139–40
        oi and *oy*, 163–64
        ô sound, 157–58
        ost, oth, oft, oss, 153
        ou and *ow*, 159–62
        review, 166, 231–32, 235
        r-influenced vowel *ar*, 145–46
        r-influenced vowel *or*, 143–44
        r-influenced vowels, 143–50
        r-influenced vowels *er, ir, ur*, 147–48
        short-vowel digraph /o͝o/, 137–40

Photo Credits

The following agencies and individuals have furnished materials to meet the photographic needs of this textbook. We wish to express our gratitude to them for their important contribution.

Tom Berg
Corbis
COREL Corporation
George Bush Presidential Library
Grand Canyon National Park
Hemera Technologies, Inc.
JUPITERIMAGES
Deborah King
Joyce Landis

Library of Congress
Greg Moss
Susan Perry
PhotoDisc/Getty Images
Photos.com
PictureQuest
Scholar Craft Products
Robin Scroggins
Martha J. Smith

Carla Thomas
Unusual Films
USDA
U.S. Fish and Wildlife Service
U.S. Geological Survey
www.forestryimages.org
www.fotolia.com
www.istockphoto.com

Unit 1

©2006 Hemera Technologies, Inc. All rights reserved. 3 (harp, bell, ring, keys), 4 (flower), 5 (horse, ball, flute, arm, top, hotdog, clown), 6 (horn), 8 (man, roof); 10 (bottle, balloon, robot, ladder); 11 (hill, carrots, hammer, button), 12 (lock, tack, brick, block), 13 (flute, plant), 14 (golf club), 15 (bread, frown, dripping faucet), 17 (scale, boy smiling, sky, skates), 19 (brick), 20 (plug), 21 (flower, skates), 23 (kangaroo), 24 (spoon, spring, stroller), 25 (trunk), 26 (bulb, gift, elk), 27 (band, golf ball and club), 31 (chair), 32 (thimble, whip), 33 (trash, beach, path, dish), 34 (ship), 35 (church, whip), 36 (path, trash, bench), 37 (spider, shirt, church), 38 (dish, plant, teeth), 39 (band, trunk, strawberries), 40 (chair, mother); www.istockphoto.com 3 (turtle, windmill, piano, dog, zebra, van), 4 (horse, jump rope, sand, gift, deer, quilt), 5 (glove, maze, clock), 6 (box, gumballs, bread, bag, goat, bowl, cap, gumdrop, tub), 8 (log, jar, pig, bed, foot, hat, tail), 10 (honey, camel, clover, zipper, boxes), 11 (egg, cross, bell, addition problem), 12 (stick, sticker, wrecker, chicken, rocket), 13 (glasses, fly, plum), 14 (clam, blender, playground), 15 (pretzel, prize, trash), 17 (scarf, snowman, squirrel, stool), 19 (blimp, spray), 20 (snap, trap, spill, drill, glass), 21 (plum, crown, clam, slide), 23 (sock, kite, stick, honey, muffin), 24 (glass, pretzel, bread, crust, drain, scrubbing), 25 (craft, camel, bunk, ramp), 26 (raft, stamp, belt, ant, drink, shield), 27 (nest, swept, tent, sink), 28 (mint, quilt, gulp, ice-cream cone, grasp), 29 (raft, children in line, boy squinting, crust, mending, straps), 30 (tusk, camel, blender, press, princess, medicine dropper), 31 (chips, shelf, shed), 32 (whistle, whiskers, wheel), 33 (baby in bathtub, peach), 34 (moth, chips), 35 (shield, chain, shoes, chocolate), 36 (wreath, branch, brush, bath), 37 (track, frog, chicken, peach, bank), 38 (spinning top, brush, sink), 39 (muffin, necklace, stamp, slide, truck, stool), 40 (branch, whistle, porch, cherry); ©2006 JUPITERIMAGES/Photos.com. All rights reserved. 3 (feather), 4 (nail, lemon), 6 (ear, leaf), 10 (berries), 13 (slippers, plate), 14 (clock), 15 (trumpet, cradle), 17 (slippers), 19 (squash), 21 (squash, stone), 23 (pillow), 27 (lamp), 29 (baby crawling, steps), 31 (cheese, shell, chin), 32 (wheelchair, throne), 34 (chin), 35 (chipmunk, thistle), 37 (lamp), 38 (blocks), 39 (backpack), 40 (shell); PhotoDisc/Getty Images 4 (monkey, tiger, bat); 10 (tiger), 11 (cliff), 13 (blanket, clouds), 14 (flock, sled), 15 (bridge, crayon), 17 (sled, snail, stairs), 19 (grill, crib, cliff), 20 (flag), 21 (blanket, drum, snake), 23 (kitchen, rock), 24 (snail), 25 (skunk, milk), 28 (grocery list, camp), 29 (flag), 31 (chimp, sheep), 34 (flash, shop), 36 (lunch), 38 (skunk), 39 (sprinkler), 40 (sheep, mushrooms, chalk); Unusual Films 10 (puppet), 25 (hands), 30 (hands), 32 (thumb), 40 (thumb); Joyce Landis 13 (class), 14 (clay), 20 (stem), 32 (thorn), 40 (thorn); © Royalty-Free/Corbis 14 (blast), 31 (ship); USDA Photo by Scott Bauer 20 (crop); Courtesy Scholar Craft Products 26 (desk); Carla Thomas 27 (mask), 39 (butter); Deborah King 28 (text); Susan Perry 30 (stomp); COREL Corporation 30 (train), 31 (shark); U.S. Fish and Wildlife Service 33 (fish), 36 (fish); Greg Moss 34 (crash); © 2006 Burke/Triolo/Brand X Pictures/PictureQuest, a division of JupiterImages Corporation 34 (cash); Gary Bernon, USDA APHIS, www.forestryimages.org 38 (slug)

Unit 2

©2006 Hemera Technologies, Inc. All rights reserved. 43 (castle, crab, band, cast, shoes), 44 (glass, jacks, cans), 45 (eggs, bell), 47 (grin), 49 (corn cob, dock), 53 (bottle), 54 (crab, chin), 57 (bottle, handle, apple), 58 (bundle, thimble), 59 (three apples, ankle), 68 (apple, jacks); www.istockphoto.com 43 (dog, bear, cupcake, seesaw, candy), 44 (trash can, clothes rack, plant, raft), 45 (can, net, bench, rabbit, elephant, neck, muffin), 49 (pot, robin, socks, rock, clock, hotdog), 52 (stump, gum, nuts, plum, plug, duck, puppy, bug, mug, bus, camel), 53 (pig, hat, rug, tub, bed, lamp), 54 (nest, twins, lock, trunk, sled, mask, drill), 57 (cattle, fiddle, speckled egg, mother and child, rattle, pickle), 58 (candle, griddle, puzzle, paddle, puddle, buckle), 59 (jingle bells, teakettle, jungle, cupcake, wobble, scribbles), 60 (cat, sock, fan, sink, wig, tent, fox, clam, nut), 67 (all photos), 68 (all photos except apple and jacks); ©2006 JUPITERIMAGES/Photos.com. All rights reserved. 43 (backpack), 44 (pants); PhotoDisc/ Getty Images 43 (stamp), 44 (cats), 54 (crib), 59 (dogs); Unusual Films 44 (fish tank), 46 (hands); U.S. Fish and Wildlife Service 49 (ox); © Royalty-Free/Corbis 52 (mud); Carla Thomas 58 (ruffle); Courtesy Scholar Craft Products 60 (desk); COREL Corporation 60 (sun)

Unit 3

PhotoDisc/Getty Images 71 (cat), 73 (snail, tail), 77 (bee), 78 (seashell, queen), 85 (lion, bridge), 86 (dime), 91 (bow and arrow, clover, dog), 92 (stone), 93 (goat, snow, toad, boat, road), 95 (bow), 99 (bus, tuba), 100 (cub), 102 (glue, bee), 103 (mule), 107 (sky), 112 (snowy owl), 113 (bolt), 125 (dime), 4 (booklet page), 132 (city); ©2006 Hemera Technologies, Inc. All rights reserved. 71 (watch, cake, gate, gas can, lock), 73 (mail, train), 77 (jet, men, tree), 78 (feet, leash, beach), 85 (Bible, tiger), 86 (bike), 87 (nighttime, lightning, fight), 91 (robot, frog, pot, fox), 92 (nose, rose, bone), 93 (coat), 95 (mow, hole), 99 (book, music, cup), 100 (flute), 102 (skates, cake, bone, coat, lime), 103 (bike), 107 (fly, tray), 125 (feet, plane), 131, 132 (field, cage, sunny); www.istockphoto.com 71 (vase, lake, pillow), 73 (chain, paint can, braid, pail, drain), 77 (beaver, pen, jeep, hen, seeds), 78 (peach, beans, tea, peacock, seagull, leaf), 85 (pickle, kitten, slippers, pie, icicles, tie, rice), 86 (slide, clock, windmill, hive, stripe, kite, fill, pine), 87 (high, Dwight, nightlight, highway, midnight), 91 (log, sock, snowman, motorcycle), 92 (cone, hose, stove), 93 (bowl, soap, oats), 95 (toast, yoke, goal), 99 (rug, duck), 102 (seeds, vase, tie), 103 (hose), 107 (fry, cry, shy, play, pray, spy), 112 (spider monkey), 113 (colt, gorilla, child, find, rind, mold), 116, 117, 125 (slide, leaf, tire), 1 (booklet page), 3 (booklet page), 132 (niece, fireplace); ©2006 JUPITERIMAGES/Photos.com. All rights reserved. 71 (plate, pray), 73 (nail, rain), 77 (lemon), 78 (peel), 92 (rope), 95 (globe, float), 99 (bowl of fruit), 103 (cape), 113 (gold necklace); Carla Thomas 71 (apron), 99 (ruler); Joyce Landis 74 (clay); COREL Corporation 87 (sunlight, flight); Unusual Films 92 (robe), 102 (cube); U.S. Fish and Wildlife Service 93 (crow), 99 (hummingbird), 2 (booklet page); USDA Photo by Scott Bauer 99 (juice); U.S. Navy photo by Aaron Burden 113 (fold)

Unit 4

PhotoDisc/Getty Images 133, 135 (roof, moon), 143, 144, 147 (turtle, nurse, bird), 153 (frost), 159 (lemon, town, flower), 160 (mouse, cow), 163 (toy truck, oyster, cowboy, coins, oinking pig), 169 (ball, hawk, king); www.istockphoto.com 135 (noodles, stool, broom, boots, pool), 136 (train), 147 (purse, girl, burn, fern), 153 (loft, cloth, moth, toss, cross), 159 (flour, ground, howl, plow, hound, compass, towel), 160 (clown, shower), 163 (boy, foil, oil), 169 (haul, cooking oil, moth); © Royalty-Free/Corbis 135 (bamboo); ©2006 JUPITERIMAGES/Photos. com. All rights reserved. 135 (spoon); Joyce Landis 147 (skirt), 163 (boil, noise); USDA Photo by Scott Bauer 147 (herd); Unusual Films 147 (verse, shirt); ©2006 Hemera Technologies, Inc. All rights reserved. 142, 159 (tower), 160 (cloud), 163 (coil); U.S. Geological Survey 6 (booklet page); Martha J. Smith 5 (booklet page); Tom Berg 7 (booklet page); Grand Canyon National Park 169 (Grand Canyon)

Unit 5

©2006 Hemera Technologies, Inc. All rights reserved. 173, 185; Library of Congress 181; PhotoDisc/Getty Images 186, booklet pages 2, 8; U.S. Fish and Wildlife Service 190 (top); www.istockphoto.com 190 (bottom), booklet pages 4, 5, 6; George Bush Presidential Library 200; ©2006 JUPITERIMAGES/Photos.com booklet page 3; Robin Scroggins booklet page 7

Unit 6

©2006 Hemera Technologies, Inc. All rights reserved. 219, 225 (phone, saxophone, toothbrush); www.istockphoto.com 225 (photograph, trophy, wheat, elephant, chicken), 226 (telephone), 229 (bottom), 239 (both); PhotoDisc/Getty Images 223, 225 (fish), 229 (top), 230 (bottom), 240; www.fotolia.com 225 (graph); Martha J. Smith 230 (top)